Contents

PREFACE

This publication is the sixth in a series aimed at helping health service staff to obtain the views of service users. It has been written for anyone who has been given this responsibility, whether in the nursing, medical, paramedical or managerial areas. The series presumes no social science background and offers a flexible approach which is very amenable to local adaptation and interpretation.

It looks·at the range of information patients and other health service users need and, drawing on the fields of public relations, patient education, health education and doctor-patient communication, provides examples of good practice.

The use of different media and the methodological issues involved in producing patient-centred information are examined.

The book also looks at the process of getting feedback from users about the quality of information provided. A list of example questions to ask users is given.

The book has been produced with funding from the Gatsby Trust.

ACKNOWLEDGEMENTS

I would like to thank Nicky Tewson for providing detailed comments on the manuscript and Philip Meredith and Bob Gann for some useful additions. My thanks go also to Madeleine Rooke-Ley for patiently typing the manuscript.

1 INTRODUCTION

One issue has surfaced repeatedly during 30 years of research on patients' views of health services: poor communication.

Research carried out as long ago as 1961 shows that patients were dissatisfied with communication and lack of information (McGee 1961; Barnes 1961). Four chapters of Cartwright (1964) dealt with the issue of staff-patient communication and described reasons for the 'unsatisfactory state of affairs'.

Despite this informative research, a recent review of consumer feedback in the NHS described numerous subsequent studies which found problems in this area. The authors commented:

> *We have certainly found no evidence of any real improvement since this problem was articulated more than twenty years ago.*
> (Jones, Leneman, Maclean, 1987, p. 85)

There seem to be a number of reasons why few improvements have been made:

★ Much of the *detailed* research has been carried out by academics and so is not easily accessible to NHS staff.

★ Most 'patient satisfaction' research carried out by NHS staff has dealt with the issue of communication and information provision in too superficial a way to enable improvements to be made.

★ There has been very little consideration of the information needs of different types of service user, those with particular conditions and those undergoing different treatments.

★ Projects to develop patient information have been isolated one-off exercises rather than planned programmes to improve communication.

★ There has been too much 'reinvention of the wheel' where uninformed attempts to improve literature for patients have resulted in material of a poor standard.

One of the most significant hindrances to better communication has been the traditional view that medical staff know 'what is best' and that patients are the passive partner in the care relationship.

There is evidence that this view has begun to change. On the one hand, this is due to research which shows that more patient control is related to better outcome (Horder and Moore, 1990). On the other hand, it is due to the current Government's reforms to the NHS which have encouraged a consumerist approach. Consumerism may have its problems when applied to the NHS (McIver, 1992) but one of its positive aspects has been the development of the Patient's Charter.

Although the charter is still a long way from being fully implemented, it has begun to raise public expectations. Patients now have some idea of what to expect when they use NHS services.

As far as information is concerned, for example, they know that they have the right:

> 'To be given a clear explanation of any treatment proposed, including any risks and any alternatives, before [they] decide whether [they] will agree to the treatment'
> and

'To be given detailed information on local health services,
including quality standards and maximum waiting times'.

In addition, they know they should be able to get information
from their local health authority about:

★ local charter standards

★ the services the health authority has arranged

★ waiting times for outpatient, day case and inpatient
    treatment by hospital, specialty and individual consultant,
    set out in a standard way

★ common diseases, conditions and treatments

★ how to complain about NHS services

★ how to maintain and improve their own health.

As relatives and friends of patients, they also know they should
be informed about the progress of treatment if this is the
patient's wish.

This is a beginning. At least users of NHS services know they
have the right to ask for certain kinds of information. Providing
good quality information to fulfil these new expectations is the
task now facing NHS staff.

Although there are some really excellent examples of patient-
centred information, the picture is patchy. There are still too
many instances of provider-led information where no attempt
has been made to assess it from the users' point of view.

This booklet examines the methodological issues involved in
producing patient-centred information and considers the
strengths and weaknesses of different ways of providing
information. It also looks at the range of information needed
and provides examples of good practice.

The final chapter deals with the process of getting feedback from users about the quality of information provided. A list of example questions to ask users is given at the end.

2 METHODOLOGICAL ISSUES

The provision of good quality information to patients relies upon a number of factors which will be covered in this chapter.

Firstly, it is important to be clear about the type of information involved. An examination of the area reveals a number of different types, such as:

★ what services are available

★ how best to use services

★ what will happen when using services

★ what standards of service to expect

★ how to stay healthy

★ about particular illnesses and diseases

★ what happens during particular operations, tests and treatments

★ self-care after operations or following diagnosis

★ the effects and side effects of drugs and treatments

★ choices of treatment.

It is useful to place these types of information on a continuum representing different levels of involvement or input from the patient.

5

Informing, Educating, Empowering

At one end of the continuum lies information which flows mostly one way, from the service provider to the service user – for example, information about services available, how best to use services or what standards to expect. The aim is to increase knowledge about a particular issue.

Patient education, however, demands more from the recipient because the aim is to change attitudes and behaviour as well as knowledge. Health education and knowledge about self-care after operations or following diagnosis of a particular illness or disease fall into this category.

Empowerment lies at the other end of the continuum, aiming to enable a person to gain greater control over a situation. The goal is to cause a range of changes in knowledge, behaviour, attitudes, skills and confidence. Helping patients to make decisions and be more involved in their health care comes into this category.

These levels of involvement can be seen as having different aims, although in practice the *type* of information (for example, health education, information about services) does not neatly fall into a single category. For instance, health education can have the aim of raising awareness about a health risk (informing) prior to changing behaviour (education).

However, it is important to be clear about the aim because different methods of transmission are involved. Whereas it may be possible to increase a person's knowledge by giving them a leaflet to read, this is likely to have no effect on their behaviour.

Similarly, showing an asthmatic person how to use an inhaler may help them to deal with a crisis, but it may take more discussion and possibly role play about how to talk to their GP before they begin to feel as if they are in control of their treatment.

Secondly, it is important to be clear about who the information is aimed at. Is it for users of a particular service? Is it for a particular care group? What are the characteristics of the people concerned? If they are elderly they may not be able to read easily because of poor eyesight. If they are on medication, in pain or in shock, their memory or concentration may be affected.

Factors such as these could affect the medium, the timing and the content of the information provided.

Thirdly, it is important to set a particular example of information provision within a wider context. One of the weaknesses of the current situation in the NHS is that information provision is patchy with regard to both the quality and coverage. As well, conflicting messages may be conveyed by various health professionals.

A project to improve information in a particular area should fit within a programme to improve communications. Taking a planned approach will aid the clarification of aims and priorities. It will also ensure that information is consistent.

For example, the communication imperatives for purchasers/commissioners will differ from those of providers/trusts/units, and GPs or professional health care staff working within organisations may have different aims again.

Health care commissioners will probably be interested in communication with their local population: some of their aims will be finding out about the needs of the different sections, telling them about which services they are purchasing and why, and empowering them to take part in a dialogue about future plans.

Service providers, on the other hand, will want to inform service users about what they provide, what to expect when they use these services and probably also (in conjunction with health care staff) about various illnesses, diseases and treatments and how to help themselves to get better after treatment.

Health care staff or professional groups will probably be particularly interested in educating patients to help them stay healthy or get better after treatment and in helping patients to take part in making choices about their treatment and to feel more in control of what is happening to them.

Fourthly, it is vitally important to construct *with* patients any information plan for patients – that is, to find out what kind of knowledge patients want, how they want it and when they want it.

This can be done by surveying, before the plan is set up, a number of patients who are to receive the information. An initial version of the plan should then be piloted by asking others to make comments about it so that it can be altered if necessary.

Fifthly, information should be assessed to make sure it is useful to the majority of those receiving it and is fulfilling the needs it was meant to address: that is, it should be monitored and evaluated.

A way to monitor the usefulness and standard of quality of the information is periodically to ask those receiving it to make comments. This is best done using a structured questionnaire, either for self-completion or by interview. Examples of questions to ask recipients are given at the end of the book.

Evaluation of the information requires assessing it in relation to the original aim and also sometimes to criteria such as cost-effectiveness or comparison with an alternative. Results gathered during monitoring can be included in an evaluation, but it is usually a more comprehensive exercise.

There are various degrees of rigour which can be applied to evaluation. At one end are experiments where as many variables as possible are controlled so that the influence or effect of the information can be measured fairly accurately.

This usually means bringing together, in a specific setting, a small number of people v·ho receive the information and a control group of people who do not, followed by the measurement of certain indicators used as outcomes, such as increased knowledge (or not, for the control group) as measured by answers to a list of questions given before and after.

Such experiments are not always useful ways of evaluating material – for example, if the aim is to affect the behaviour of people in their home setting or if it would be unethical to use a control group.

There is also the question of cost. It is probably unrealistic to expect those on tight budgets to spend large sums of money on making evaluation as rigorous as possible.

A sensible approach would be to copy evaluated material where this exists and to evaluate any new material as rigorously as funds allow. The minimum would be to try to set realistic objectives and then attempt to find out if these have been achieved.

It is worth remembering that funding organisations usually expect some kind of evaluation so that they can judge whether their money has been well spent. Those wishing to examine methods of evaluation in more detail may find StLeger, Schneiden and Walsworth-Bell (1992) useful.

If possible, it is best to follow examples of good practice rather than start from scratch. An outline of what this means has been given above and can be summarised as shown overleaf:

★ clear aim

★ targeted population

★ set within a wider communications programme

★ patient/user involvement

★ monitoring and evaluation.

In Chapter 4, some examples are given for different *types* of information provision, but in the next chapter consideration is given to *ways* of providing information.

3 WAYS OF PROVIDING INFORMATION

There are two important points to remember when considering ways of providing information. Firstly, the NHS and health professionals are only one source of knowledge for the general public.

People talk about health and receive information and advice through many other avenues, including friends and family, TV programmes, magazines, advertisements and other agencies.

The more easily the information provided by health professionals links into these informal channels and is consistent with them, the better.

Sometimes it is necessary to deal with conflicting advice, such as that given by agencies with commercial interests (tobacco, sugar, alcohol, etc.) and that deriving from religious and cultural beliefs (contraception, diet, attitudes to health and illness, etc.).

By developing information planning with patients and making the process of providing it as interactive as possible, the effectiveness is likely to increase.

There is a limit to the amount of information a person can take in at any one time, particularly if they are ill or under stress. This means that it is advisable to offer advice on more than one occasion.

Secondly, disseminating knowledge is not solely about making leaflets available, although this may well be the first option that comes to mind. A wide range of options is in fact available and it is worth considering the strengths, weaknesses and costs of each before making a choice.

Written materials

Strengths of leaflets:

★ They allow a person to read at their own pace and to return to refresh their memory whenever necessary.

★ Detailed and complex information can be given (using diagrams if necessary).

★ They can be passed to others (for example, relatives and friends) so that information is shared.

★ It should be easy to make them accessible because they can be handed out or posted at an appropriate time.

★ They can be easily and cheaply produced, although the cost will depend largely upon the design and visual presentation.

Weaknesses of leaflets:

★ They are usually mass-produced for the sake of cost and convenience and this means that they are designed for the 'average' person.

★ Not everyone is literate or able to read English and translations can be problematical.

★ There can be problems in the distribution system and those expected to hand them out may not do so.

★ They are easily lost or mislaid and not valued highly.

Although leaflets are the commonest form of information provision, research has shown that many people dislike getting information this way. For example, in research carried out by the Centre for Mass Communication Research (Budd and McCron, 1982), the general public expressed the following preferences for the means of getting health information:

Means	Percentage of people in favour
TV/Radio	33
Posters	12
GP	7
Press	6
TV advertisement	6
Leaflet	4

The picture is more complicated where a target group of people rather than the general population is concerned. For example, in a study of patients with ulcerative colitis who accepted a leaflet from their doctor, most, when asked about their preference, said they preferred a leaflet (Mayberry, Rose and Rhodes, 1989). The results were:

Method	Percentage of patients in favour
Leaflet	95
Video at clinic	15
Poster at clinic	10
Video at home	7
Audio tape	5

The design and content of the leaflet is an important consideration and there is research to support the suggestion that some designs are more acceptable than others. For example, Zweifier and Kaunisto (1989) compared two leaflets about hypertension with different formats and found that only one was successful in improving knowledge.

There is also research which suggests that workbooks are better in some instances than leaflets and that combining these with other support strategies such as a self-help group, telephone contact and a counselling session can be very effective.

Bailey et al (1990) conducted a longitudinal one-year study of asthma patients in the United States in which a group was given a self-management programme involving a workbook, a counselling session, a support group meeting and telephone contact. They were compared with 'usual care' patients who received standard asthma pamphlets.

Those patients participating in the self-management programme showed substantially better adherence to instructions as well as improved functional status when compared to 'usual care' patients. The researchers sound a note of caution, however:

> *It was difficult to balance the need to provide patients with sufficient information with the need to avoid the diluting effects of too much information. It is tempting and easy to give patients more information than they actually need or want. This temptation should be resisted . . .* (p.1668)

Leaflets are not the only type of written material - there are also posters, blackboards, whiteboards and flip-charts. Posters are useful for raising awareness or directing attention towards issues, but only a limited amount of information can be conveyed. Generally the images used must be striking in order to catch attention. This means that design and printing is important and so may well be costly.

Blackboards and whiteboards are easily cleaned and so are good for information which is likely to change, such as expected waiting times in clinics or surgeries. They are cheap, but the presentation is only as good as the skill of the person who writes on the board.

Flip-charts are a useful aid to information given personally, particularly where a small group of people is involved. They are cheap and portable but easily get torn.

Audio cassettes

Strengths:

★ Literacy not needed, so useful with those who are unable to read. Various dialects can also be more easily catered for. This is important where the dialect only exists in spoken form (e.g. Sylheti).

★ They allow a person to proceed at their own pace, as the tape can be stopped and started.

★ Detailed and complex information can be given.

★ Good for certain skills development, for example, relaxation, exercise routines.

★ Equipment is easily available.

★ Fairly cheap to reproduce.

Weaknesses:

★ Not useful with those who have hearing problems.

★ May not hold the attention as well as written material.

★ A clear, good-quality recording is essential.

★ The initial recording may be expensive if studio facilities are not available.

There are a number of examples of the use of audio tape to provide information to patients. Brian Hogbin, a consultant surgeon at Brighton General Hospital, has been using cassette recorders to tape consultations during which patients were told they had cancer. They were encouraged to take the tape home with them and an initial study showed that 85 per cent of the patients listened to the tapes, almost always together with someone else at home. More than a third said it contained information they had forgotten (Hogbin and Fallowfield, 1989).

Jenkinson et al (1988) compared the effects on the self-management of asthma of a specially prepared book and audio cassette tape with similar contents. Patients at a general practice were randomly given the book, the tape, both the book and tape, or neither.

Questionnaires on the patients' knowledge of the use of bronchodilators and prophylactic drugs (if applicable) and their perceived disability resulting from asthma were administered four times – at the start of the study, six months later (immediately before the educational material was issued), nine months later, and a year and a half after the start of the study.

Knowledge about the use of drugs was significantly increased in the groups who received the material after three months and persisted after 12 months. Patients who had been given the tape or the book and tape increased their scores of knowledge of drugs more than patients given the book alone. Interestingly, patients given both the book and the tape preferred the book, even though they learnt more from the tape.

Videos

Strengths:

★ Can reach a very wide audience because their effect is not dependent on literacy skills or, if specially designed, hearing.

★ May hold the attention better than written material or audio cassettes, particularly with audiences who prefer this medium.

★ Convey reality, particularly movement, better than many other media.

★ Can be used to stimulate discussion with small groups of people.

★ If taken home, allow a person to proceed at their own pace, as the video can be stopped and started.

★ If taken home, can be used to share information within the family.

★ Can be made accessible by non-NHS users through video shops.

★ Fairly cheap to reproduce.

Weaknesses:

★ Although many people have video recorders, those on low incomes may not.

★ Initial cost of equipment can be high.

★ Expensive to produce initial videotape master copy.

★ The type of experience and skill needed to produce a good quality master may not be readily available.

Gagliano (1988) carried out a review of articles on the use of videotapes in patient education in order to assess the efficacy of this method. She found that videos consistently increased short-term knowledge. They were found to instruct as well as, and often more effectively than, written materials, lectures or even individual counsellors. However, decay in long-term knowledge retention and compliance with instructions remained as much a problem after using videos as after using other methods.

Gagliano's most interesting finding was that studies using videotape modelling – that is, the portrayal of behaviour using 'role models' with whom viewers can identify – seemed to be very successful.

One example was a study by Melamed et al (1975) in the United States. They showed one group of inner-city children scheduled for restorative dental treatment a film in which an anxious child coped well with treatment, and a similar control group with an unrelated drawing exercise.

They found that the children who saw the film co-operated more during their treatment than did those in the control group. This finding was replicated in a later study using an unrelated videotape with the control group.

A further study by the same researchers attempted to define the factors in video that most effectively decrease anxiety and improve behaviour. They compared the effect of a peer-modelling video with that of an informational video (Melamed et al, 1978). The group which saw the modelling video reported less anxiety, showed less sympathetic arousal and behaved better during the procedure than did the information video group, although both groups did better than a control group that saw an unrelated video.

Adults have also been found to benefit from videos showing role models. Gatchel (1986) found decreased anxiety among highly and moderately fearful dental patients immediately after they saw a modelling video and six months later. Moderately fearful patients also changed their behaviour by arranging more dental appointments than did a control group who saw a lecture video.

Computers

Strengths:

★ Allow a person to proceed at their own pace.

★ Acceptable and accessible to a very wide range of people including those who are blind and those who have reading difficulties (a speaking chip can be used).

★ Scope for pictures and graphics to make complex information easier to understand.

★ Scope for people to work through simulated life situations (for example, what is likely to happen if I act like this).

★ Question and answer formats allow assessment of a person's understanding.

Weaknesses:

★ Not many homes have computers and so use is generally limited to other locations.

★ Equipment is relatively expensive.

★ Usefulness is highly dependent upon the quality of the software, particularly user-friendliness.

★ Specialised skills are needed to produce software, and staff with those skills may not be readily available.

A number of studies have shown that patients find computer terminals preferable to printed formats, and for certain issues they are more acceptable than health care professionals (Deardoff, 1986). Computers have also been found to be superior to both oral and written communication in terms of knowledge improvement (Luker and Caress, 1989).

Stanley and Tongue (1991) describe a study using the ELFIN system of computer software, which provides a broad range of information about health on a patient-dedicated terminal in general practice waiting areas. Experience of the system at four contrasting sites in Merseyside is reported.

The researchers found that on a five-point scale from very hard to very easy to use, between 43 per cent and 58 per cent of users across the four sites rated the system as very easy to use and only 13-18 per cent as very hard.

Other Ways

There are two other main ways of providing information: personally and by telephone.

Most people have a phone, although the proportion drops markedly for the lowest socio-economic group. Nevertheless, telephone-based information systems are popular and have been used to inform people on a wide range of subjects.

There have been a few studies examining the value of using telephones as a way of giving information about health. Stevens Garding et al (1988) looked at the use of phone calls to provide information to patients suffering from myocardial infarction.

All patients were given information in hospital, but after discharge, one group received three phone calls in two months repeating the information given earlier and a control group received no calls. The group of patients who were telephoned and given a repeat of the information were found to have better knowledge.

In another study, Weinberger et al (1989) looked at ways of providing information to patients with osteoarthritis. After the researchers had assessed the functional status of the 439 patients in the study, they were randomly assigned to one of three intervention groups or to a control group.

Of the three intervention groups, one received information by phone, one in person at the clinic and one both by phone and in person.

The telephone intervention had a clear beneficial effect on patients' functional status. Those who received telephone contacts had significantly improved scores for physical disability and pain, as well as a trend towards improved psychological status. Telephone contact was associated with an improvement of approximately 10 per cent in functional status scores, compared with patients who were not contacted by telephone.

Among those contacted only at the clinic, physical health worsened but neither pain nor psychological health differed from those of patients not contacted at the clinic. This was an unexpected finding and the researchers had trouble explaining it. However, among their suggestions was that the clinic might not be the best place to provide information because often patients are too ill when they attend to pay much attention to the information offered.

Information can be provided personally to individuals alone or to groups. Research in this area shows that in many cases it does not make a great deal of difference either way.

For examples, Lindeman (1972) randomly assigned all surgical patients admitted during the same week (35) to either individual or group pre-operative instruction. The results showed no significant difference on post-operative ventilatory function scores adjusted for pre-operative ventilatory function and no difference on number of post-operative analgesics administered.

Providing information to a group will usually involve less time than to the same number of individuals and so, in many circumstances, group education can be cost effective.

Community health development workers have found that by going out and contacting people in the places where they usually meet, they can find out what kind of health needs, including information needs, they have. Workers can also develop opportunities to discuss health issues and convey information in these settings (NCHR, 1987; Adams et al, 1990).

Translations

Those whose first language is not English are seriously disadvantaged when information is provided only in English. However, obtaining good quality translations can be difficult. The unwary can find themselves with a translated leaflet which is full of errors.

Many of the problems can be avoided by using experienced translators, checking the information with health professionals who read the language and have experience of the information being given and by piloting the leaflet among potential readers. A booklet produced by NE Thames Regional Health Authority gives guidance on producing health information for non-English-speaking people (NE Thames RHA, 1990).

Many non-English-speaking people are illiterate in their own language, and so it will also be necessary to provide interpreters, health advocates and link workers.

Finally, it is worth pointing out that providing appropriate information for Black people is not only about making sure that the needs of people who do not speak English are catered for. It is also about providing all health information in a culturally heterogeneous way.

This can be done by several means – for instance, by using illustrations and examples which draw upon a range of cultural perspectives and by finding out the particular needs and concerns of different Black groups before providing them with appropriate information which fits into their lifestyles and beliefs.

The Health Education Authority has co-ordinated the production of a wide range of health promotion materials for Black people (see 'Useful addresses').

Summary

The more easily information links into the informal channels that people use to receive it, the better it is likely to be received. Leaflets are not the only option. There are a number of ways of providing information to patients and the strengths and weaknesses of the different media should be considered before a choice is made. The most appropriate medium will be the one best suited to the type of information, the type of patient, the budget available and the circumstances in which the information will be given. It may be best to use a combination of different media and to offer the information on a number of occasions.

4 EXAMPLES OF TYPES OF INFORMATION

General resources

When Elaine Kempson carried out her review of consumer health information services in the early 1980s (Kempson, 1984) they were in their infancy in Britain compared with Europe, North America and Australia.

She recommended that the NHS should provide funds for a specialist consumer health information resource unit within each regional health authority.

Regional health information services were established in 1992 with the aim of giving information on:

★ NHS services available

★ waiting times for outpatient, day case and inpatient treatment by hospital, specialty and individual consultant, set out in a standard way

★ common diseases, conditions and treatments

★ how to complain about NHS services

★ how to maintain and improve your own health.

The model for these services was the Help for Health Trust, an independent charity established by Wessex Regional Health

Authority (see 'Useful addresses'). Help for Health started as a research project in 1979 and became established as a regional resource in 1982. It became an independent registered charity in 1991. Its aim is to provide:

> *. . . an information service and not an advisory or support system.*
> *The object is to provide people with the knowledge they need to*
> *make their own choices.*
> (Alderman, 1991)

The national self-help database 'Helpbox' contains records of national voluntary organisations and groups, details of self-help and popular medical books and self-help leaflets and similar 'grey literature'.

Patients, their families and health care staff can contact the service by telephone, letter or in person and information is provided free of charge. Training and consultancy are also available on a contract basis.

At the end of 1991 the NHS Communications Exchange Database was set up at Help for Health and during 1993 this is concentrating on information about projects linked to Patient's Charter standards, as part of the NHS Management Executive's Benchmarking Project.

The Help for Health Trust is also involved in a project with the Isle of Wight Health Authority to develop and evaluate the impact of a model health-promoting ward. The Acorn Project (see 'Useful addresses') is being carried out at St Mary's Hospital and involves:

★ the establishment of a patient education resource centre

★ the development of an information pack for patients giving details of their condition, treatment and care

★ training for nurses and other health care staff to enhance communication with patients

★ ensuring that patients have continuing access to information about self-care, healthy lifestyles and community resources after discharge

★ evaluating the effectiveness of the patient education activities.

Another useful resource for health care staff involved in information provision is the Consumer Health Information Consortium (CHIC - see 'Useful addresses'). This is a network of people and organisations involved in making information about all aspects of health and health services available to the public. CHIC has produced a 1992 Directory of Consumer Health Information Services in the UK.

Examples of local health information services are also given by Robinson and Roberts (1985), Sweetland (1990) and Hicks (1991). Further details about the development of health information generally can be found in Gann and Needham, 1991, and Gann, 1991.

Looking at communications at the strategic level, a research and development project at Mid-Downs Health Authority starts from the premise that communications need to be 'planned, deliberate and disciplined if they are to be successful' (SW Thames RHA/Mid Downs HA, 1992).

The project involves:

★ mapping the routes by which a district health authority, as a purchaser of health care, can most effectively communicate with its audiences and sustain dialogues with them

★ identifying the best methods for doing so, according to the importance of the subject to the authority and its relevance to the audience(s)

★ producing a communications action plan for the authority

★ developing and disseminating models of good communications practice related to various scenarios, events and episodes in the life of the authority.

A communications strategy is important because it sets information provision within the wider context of communication within an organisation and between it and its contacts or users.

It also allows for the fact that the information provided by an organisation can be supported, or not - perhaps even contradicted or negated - by policies, procedures and practices of that organisation (or others).

For example, the Patient's Charter states that every citizen has the right to be given a clear explanation of any treatment proposed, including any risks and alternatives, before they agree to treatment. It is difficult to imagine how this can be achieved with people who do not speak English if trained interpreters are not readily available.

Whatever the content of the information, there is plenty of advice available on how to present it clearly and accessibly in a written form. There is no excuse for badly written and presented information when guidelines such as those produced by Silver (1991), North Manchester Health Authority (1991) and Glasser (1992) are available. Public relations and health promotion departments can also help.

Glasser (1992) for example, includes:

Style: keep it short. This applies to every level: words, sentences, paragraphs and whole texts.

Tone: convey a friendly, welcoming message, but avoid being too light-hearted and chatty. Be careful with using colloquial or informal language. Avoid jargon.

Illustrations: avoid borrowing directly from textbooks. Produce a simplified version. A bad illustration is worse than no illustration at all.

Layout: use space - allow plenty of white on every page and between lines and paragraphs. Think about different formats. Provide clear headings.

Colours and typefaces: bear in mind the use of different colours of paper and ink. Check if there is a policy on use of particular typefaces.

Most important of all: try out a version of the printed information on those it is aimed at or, even better, include members of the target audience in planning the design.

There are many examples of different types of health information produced within the NHS and some of these will be described shortly. It is worth pointing out, however, that the NHS may not be producing all the types of health information that people need.

The medical journalist Claire Rayner analysed 40,000 letters she received each year and identified nine categories of queries about health care problems which are not adequately dealt with by the NHS (Rayner, 1979).

The letters are not a representative sample of the general population because they are from people who read the magazines in question and who choose to write, but they give an indication of the worries of a large number of people. She identified:

(a) Anatomy and physiology queries, mostly from young people.

(b) Illness queries, such as what terms like angina and fibroids mean; what will happen in a particular surgical procedure;

what a particular diagnosis such as epilepsy or Parkinson's disease means.

(c) Anxieties about pregnancy and childbirth.

(d) Birth control problems.

(e) Child care problems.

(f) Mental health problems.

(g) The problems of old people.

(h) Sexual problems.

(i) Needs for plastic surgery.

A more recent attempt to look at health information needs from the perspective of the health service user identified a number of gaps:

> *It is evident that the information currently available to anyone choosing a general practitioner is inadequate. Information on hospital services is even more sketchy. Inpatient handbooks or guides to services provided by the NHS are too often produced with the aim of creating compliant rather than informed patients. Information is usually too general to be of use to individual patients and is often out of date shortly after costly publication. Little of what is offered allows patients to make choices or to question the services provided, and there is little consensus in the NHS about what further information should be made available.*
> (Winkler, 1990)

The Patient's Charter may encourage the development of information to fill some of these gaps, but as well as developing plans based upon existing good practice, research needs to be carried out to identify the unfulfilled information needs of health service users.

It is also wise not to assume that if information has been produced for people about an issue, their knowledge about this will have increased. The people concerned may not have received the data or, for various reasons, it may not have been assimilated by them.

For example, despite the fact that each household in Scotland was issued with an explanatory booklet about the NHS reforms, a questionnaire survey carried out by GPs in Renfrewshire discovered that only 10 per cent of respondents showed evidence of understanding the changes (McIntyre, Miller, Sullivan, 1992).

All patients attending morning surgery during one week in September 1990 (a total of 237) were asked to complete a short questionnaire and 174 completed it.

There was a high level of misunderstanding over the terms 'minor surgery' and 'child health surveillance' which the authors thought might lead to under-utilisation of these services.

Some information, such as that about changes in NHS services, may need to be given as part of a more intensive public campaign. An example is that organised by Trent Regional Health Authority (Hull, 1990).

As a result of a survey which collected details of the concerns of the public in Trent region about the proposed NHS changes, Trent RHA took the 12 aspects which worried people most and turned them into 12 individual question-and-answer fact sheets which were distributed within the region.

Altogether 67,000 sets of the English version were printed and distributed. Copies were also printed in other languages and on an audio tape for blind people.

The most popular leaflets at the regional headquarters (taken by staff and visitors) were those relating to changes affecting general practitioner services.

Information about services

In 1979 the Royal Commission on the National Health Service recommended that every hospital should provide explanatory booklets for patients about the hospital and its routine.

Like many other health authorities, Brighton has over the years produced a variety of booklets and leaflets to comply with this. Unlike most others, however, Brighton decided to evaluate this literature to find out if it met the needs of those it was intended to inform.

The evaluation was carried out by the Royal Institute of Public Administration Consultancy Services (RIPACS), which produced a report in 1987.

The evaluation involved investigating:

1   The literature distribution process to find out whether it was working efficiently.

2   Examining the accessibility of the content and design by comparing the literature with other examples, by readability tests and by asking patients.

3   Examining the comparative differences in the costs of producing information booklets (RIPACS, 1987).

It is not always necessary to employ an outside consultancy to evaluate information provision, although a degree of objectivity is required. A different approach would be to set up a multidisciplinary working group including patient representatives, such as CHC members. It would still be important to ask a sample of patients for their views, however, and also to obtain advice about design.

Another way of tacking the issue would be to employ a researcher. This approach was taken by a quality assurance group working on the Otterburn Ward, an acute psychiatric ward, at St George's Hospital, Morpeth, in Northumberland.

The group obtained funds from the Northern Regional Health Authority and a researcher was appointed in 1990 with the aims of:

1 Finding out the information needs of patients and staff in Otterburn Ward.

2 Producing a new information booklet.

3 Doing follow-up research and making general recommendations for improving patient information in other parts of the hospital (Cutts, 1991).

The researcher interviewed more than 30 patients, using a semi-structured, topic-led approach with the aim of finding out:

> . . . *how well they felt they were informed, whether their anxieties were eased by being given clear information, whether their relatives were given information and help, what they thought of the environment of the ward and what their opinion was of the first patient information booklet.*
> (Cutts, 1991, p.4)

Nearly all the patients said they had not read the existing booklet. Most said that when they first came in they were too ill to think about it and then later it seemed no longer necessary to read it.

They agreed that it might have helped if their key worker had gone through it with them at the right time during their treatment.

Patients made it clear also that they preferred receiving information through conversations with staff, leading the researcher to conclude that it would be better if certain parts of the booklet were used as triggers for verbal explanation rather than presented explicitly.

The results of the research was a new booklet following a question-and-answer format using the kinds of questions patients ask in the order they tended to ask them, for example:

★ What is this handbook for?

★ What are the visiting arrangements?

★ What is Otterburn House?

★ What about my money?

★ . . . and my DSS benefits?

★ How long will I be here?

★ Who works on the ward?

★ What are my rights as a patient?

★ How do I make a complaint?

A 'story-line' approach using the headings 'Settling in', 'Living in Otterburn' and 'Leaving' was followed and pictures and cartoons were used to get information across.

It is interesting to note that the researcher and the Quality Assurance Group agreed:

> . . . *that a booklet would be useful, but only in the context of a wider patient information strategy.*
> (Cutts, 1991, p.2)

The booklet was linked to other sources of information in the ward and was designed to be a useful tool for key workers in their talks with patients.

The research also recommended that the *patient* information strategy should be linked to an improved *wider* information strategy covering not only patients but also information for staff and details of the buildings and environment (for example, who works where and how to get around so that familiarity develops easily).

Many excellent examples of smart, professionally produced booklets about hospital services are currently available, but when examining them it is wise to remember that they are only as good as their usefulness to patients and the context in which they are supplied.

That is, do they provide the information patients want and do they do so within an information-giving environment which supports and reinforces that provided by the booklets?

There is also the question of their value to particular groups of users. For example, a survey of patients at Sunderland Eye Infirmary found that 70 per cent of patients could not read the health authority admission booklet because of eye conditions (Gilley, 1990).

The booklet was also found to be out of date and, because it was written for the whole district, it contained a good deal of unnecessary detail without giving the information the infirmary patients required.

A new booklet was designed which was printed in large type in a 12-page format with a full colour cover and a small number were ordered so that it could be updated regularly.

As a result of their review of patient information, Sunderland Eye Infirmary also produced an outpatient booklet, new appointment cards and a squint booklet. Their concern for different types of patient has led them to consider producing a booklet for children and information on audio cassettes for those patients who cannot read even the large-print booklets.

Given the history of academic research on the doctor-patient relationship, it is no surprise to find that controlled trials to measure the effectiveness of leaflets about services are more common in primary health care than other services.

For example Marsh (1980) reported a study aimed at finding out:

1   How patients viewed the purpose and value of the
     brochure and whether they had any ideas for improving it.

2   Whether receipt of the brochure resulted in greater
     awareness of the staff and facilities of the primary health
     care team.

3   Whether it modified the way in which patients might use
     the range of services.

For the purpose of the evaluation, it was decided to study
women patients aged between 18 and 55 because they were
fairly frequent users of the whole range of services. Two groups
were chosen – women newly registered at the Centre (262) and
those who had been registered for at least three years (253). Half
of each group were given a copy of the brochure.

Two or three weeks later all the patients were followed up in
their own homes by one of three interviewers employed by the
research and intelligence unit of Cleveland County Council,
who asked a series of questions.

One of these was to imagine certain health problems and say
what they would probably do if faced with them. This was only
a crude predictor of actual behaviour, but because of time
structures it was impossible to follow up the patients over a
long period to measure actual changes in behaviour.

The results showed that 98 per cent of both new and established
patients who had read the brochure found no difficulty in
understanding it. A few had suggestions for improving it.

Seventy-three per cent of new and 55 per cent of established
patients said that they found out something they did not
already know; 64 per cent of new patients had not realised the
variety of services available; 24 per cent of established patients
said they did not know that marriage guidance counsellors
were available at the centre.

Patients' responses to the three hypothetical problems showed a significant swing (over 10 per cent) to seeing the nurse and an associated trend away from seeing the doctor after reading the practice brochure.

The author writes:

> *Most important. . . is the evidence in the results that reading the brochure improved the accuracy in the way patients would use the various members of the primary health care team.*
> (Marsh, 1980, p.731)

A slightly different approach to the same issue was reported by Nevell and Mason (1987). In order to evaluate their patient information leaflet about services, they asked patients to complete a questionnaire designed to test knowledge about the practice before and after receiving the leaflet.

The study is reported as a pilot, so only 70 patients were involved. These were patients who attended the surgery during a three-month period and who were subsequently scheduled to return for a review appointment within two months.

The patients completed the questionnaire at their first visit and then received a practice leaflet. When they returned for their review appointment, the questionnaire was again administered and patients were asked for their comments on the leaflet and any suggestions for its improvement. A similar procedure was adopted at home visits.

The results showed that for most questions the proportion of correct responses increased over time and there was a significant improvement in overall scores between the two questionnaires.

There was no measurable change in the pattern of behaviour for repeat prescriptions, out-of-hours visits or attendance for baby checks and immunisations, but attendance at the monthly 'warts and verrucas' sessions increased and three patients said this was as a result of information in the leaflet. Two women changed their pattern of advice-seeking from the local family planning clinic to the practice as a result of the leaflet.

A more comprehensive evaluation of a practice information leaflet is described by Bhopal et al (1990). The evaluation had a number of elements which were carried out before and after the distribution of 5,000 practice leaflets given out over a 10-month period: These elements were:

1   A self-completion questionnaire assessing knowledge of the practice.

2   Specifying sex of each patient and the date, time and reason for the consultation

3   Monitoring of time and reason for incoming calls.

Before the leaflets were distributed, 250 patients attending the surgery were invited to complete the questionnaire and 200 questionnaires were posted to a systematic sample of patients. Details of consultations were monitored for 18 weeks and incoming calls were monitored for 9 weeks.

After the leaflet distribution, every third patient visiting the surgery was invited to complete the questionnaire (253 of whom had seen the leaflet and 99 who had not), and 300 were mailed to a sample of patients.

The results showed that the knowledge scores of the group who had seen the leaflet were significantly higher than the baseline study group and the group who had not seen the leaflet.

The leaflet had a small impact on patients' behaviour in that 37 per cent of 416 new consultations with practice nurses were self-referrals in the follow-up study, compared with 29.5 per cent of 227 in the baseline study, an increase of 7.5 per cent.

The percentage of calls between 12 noon and 4pm increased from 11 per cent in the baseline study to 17.5 per cent in the follow-up study, an increase of 6.5 per cent.

Information at discharge

Although for many years there has been a widely recognised need for booklets giving patients and relatives details about what to expect from hospital and other services, until recently there has been little recognition of a need for written information on discharge from hospital.

Research has shown quite clearly the kind of information patients need. For example, qualitative research carried out by the British Market Research Bureau for Eastbourne, Brighton and Hastings health authorities (British Market Research Bureau, 1991) found that patients wanted notes and advice to take home to ease any anxiety about being away from immediate medical care, any further appointment clearly given in writing and a letter to take to their GP.

When the researchers carried out a large-scale (quantitative) survey, they found that although 86 per cent of respondents had been given instructions about what should and should not be done on leaving hospital, only 28 per cent of these had received written information. Also, 20 per cent had received no instructions at all.

A trial of a discharge booklet was reported by Sandler et al (1989). One hundred and fifty eight patients being discharged from hospital were alternately allocated to receive a booklet or not to receive it.

At their first attendance at the outpatient clinic after their discharge they were given a questionnaire to assess their knowledge of aspects of their discharge, such as why they were in hospital, the name of their consultant, the names of the drugs they were prescribed, the frequency of the dose and the reasons they were taking each drug.

Of patients who received the booklet, 86 per cent knew the names of their drugs, 95 per cent the frequency of the dose and 85 per cent the reasons for taking each drug, compared with 47 per cent, 58 per cent and 42 per cent respectively for the control group who did not receive it.

The researchers concluded:

> *Giving patients an information booklet at discharge from hospital appreciably increased the accuracy and thoroughness of their recall of important medical details concerning their illness and its treatment. The booklet was shown to be feasible, helpful in the outpatients clinic, and preferred by most general practitioners.*
> (Sandler et al, 1989, p.870)

Medical records and letters

Information about patients which is passed between different parts of the NHS has traditionally been kept from patients. Since 1984 patients have had access to their computerised medical records and since the end of 1991 they have also had access to their written records.

This is a relatively new practice in Britain but 20 years ago in the United States, Shenkin and Warner (1973) concluded that open access to medical records would improve patients' adherence to treatment, improve the efficiency of the service and strengthen the role of the profession.

There have been a number of recent British reports of studies looking at access to letters and records. For example, Rutherford and Gabriel (1991) investigated whether routine clinic letters might be of interest to the patients concerned and if so, whether they would wish to see further correspondence.

The researchers conducted a postal questionnaire survey of 201 patients who attended general renal outpatient clinics over one year. Each was sent a questionnaire asking whether the enclosed letter was of interest, understandable, accurate and whether copies of further letters were wanted. Comments were also requested.

A copy of the questionnaire with an explanatory letter was also sent to the patients' GPs.

Questionnaires were returned by 94 per cent of patients, 25 per cent of whom needed reminding.

The researchers found that 96 per cent of responding patients were pleased to receive copies of their outpatient medical correspondence and 93 per cent of these asked for copies of any subsequent letters.

Of the 180 completed questionnaires, 120 patients wrote a total of 133 comments. No overtly critical comments were received, the three most common categories being 'happy with care/thank you' (28 per cent), 'do not understand medical terms/need more simple explanations' (28 per cent) and 'good idea' (19 per cent).

Fifteen people corrected a factual error and three people felt the information they had been given could have been upsetting.

A similar study was carried out by Rylance (1990). He carried out a pilot study of parents' reactions and responses to copies of all correspondence relating to the care of their children as outpatients.

Of the 253 families who were sent copies in this way, replies were received from 224. Of these, 222 replied that the practice was helpful, that it made them less worried and that they wanted it to be repeated.

Rylance comments:

> *With this practice I have not needed to change the content, nature*
> *or sentiment of any letter I have wanted to write, perhaps because*
> *the content is only that which would have been fully discussed*
> *directly in the clinic, and I have not excluded any patient episodes*
> *or letters from this practice.*
> (Rylance, 1990, p.609)

This may not apply to all circumstances and there has been
some concern about psychiatric patients in particular.

Bernadt, Gunning and Quenstedt (1991) recruited 72 consecutive
general adult psychiatric outpatients and got them firstly to rate
the routine face-to-face clinical interviews they had received and
then rate the main written clinical summary about themselves
which had originally been sent to their general practitioners.

There were matched questions concerning understanding,
accuracy, omissions, upset caused, wrong emphasis, opinion on
access, helpful information, and outlook.

Thirty-two patients were posted their inpatient summary, 31 the
outpatient letter that had been written after their first
attendance, and nine a domiciliary visit letter. Patients did not
have access to other parts of their records.

For their main written summary, patients gave favourable
ratings for most questions but only 51 per cent rated the written
assessment as having provided helpful information and 28 per
cent were upset by what they had read.

The researchers' finding that only about half of patients thought
that the written summary provided helpful information agrees
with a study of rheumatology outpatients in which only 20 out
of 42 patients gave a favourable rating for the amount of
information provided by the physician's letter (Gill and Scott,
1986).

Views on the benefits to psychiatric patients are divided, however. Parrot, Strathdee and Brown (1988) found that forensic patients given access to the daily record made by all disciplines thought that they were better able to discuss their problems with staff and better able to put forward their own views. They considered also that access enabled them to correct errors.

Others have argued that the short-term distress suffered by some psychiatric patients may in the long term be therapeutic (Stoller, 1988).

Information contained in medical records and letters, and much of the information given at discharge, is about diagnosis and treatment. As such it would appear to be qualitatively different from information about services available, because it is personal to the individual patient.

This type of patient information provision is best described as patient education because it involves more than just the straight-forward transmission of information.

Patient education

The division is not precise, but it is possible to see differences between information provision and patient education. Information to patients about what services are available, including how best to use these services and what standards to expect, appears to be the only main area of patient information which is impersonal – that is, not tailor-made for each individual.

In a useful learning package, 'Patient Education and Information Giving', produced by Sandwell Hospitals and Community Health Service in conjunction with West Midlands Regional Health Authority, Ann Close writes:

> *Many people, including health care professionals, equate patient education with giving patient information. . . . Giving*

information and passing on facts does not ensure that the patient will learn. . . . Information giving is therefore a small but important part of patient education.
(Close, 1993)

This package covers the whole range of activities associated with patient education, including: definitions; planning at strategic and operational level; the needs of different patient populations, and patient education activities and programmes.

There is a large amount of literature available on the subject of patient education and it is not the purpose of this booklet to cover this in any detail. Literature reviews are available for those who wish to pursue the subject (e.g., Cohen 1981; Crane, 1985).

The aim here is to look at some examples of different types of patient education in order to give the reader an idea of the range and scope of the area.

Surgical care

The value of pre-operative preparation for patients was recognised many years ago. In 1977, Boore wrote:

Most nurses will agreed that surgical patients should be given information about their circumstances and prospective treatment and care, and that they should be taught deep-breathing and leg exercises.
(Boore, 1977, p.409)

However, she complained that the instruction given was often unplanned and inadequate.

More recently, leaflets have been developed for patients undergoing particular types of surgery. For example, Bunker (1983) describes a study which set out to discover the kind of information wanted by patients who had recently undergone transurethral resection of the prostate.

Fifty-seven patients (average age of 71 years) were asked to read a leaflet and at the follow-up appointment fill in a questionnaire asking questions about the leaflet and the information within it and the patients' experience of surgery.

Of the 50 completed questionnaires, 82 per cent would have liked to have been given the information leaflet to read before their operation. The piece of information most patients wanted was the estimated length of stay in hospital (83 per cent).

Only 20 per cent had the effect of the operation on their sex life explained to them, whereas more than 50 per cent thought this was important, and 79 per cent of men under the age of 70 thought this aspect was important.

Nearly everyone (98 per cent) remembered being told to drink plenty, showing that recall was good and indicating that it was likely that other items were remembered correctly.

Leaflets describing 65 general surgical operations have been developed by the department of surgery at Friarage Hospital, Northallerton. Each leaflet consists of a description of an illness, an operation, preoperative care, recovery in hospital and, after discharge from hospital, common complications and outlook. Edwards (1990) reports on a study to assess the reaction of a sample of patients to the leaflet provided.

A questionnaire asking about satisfaction with information provision was given to patients at their first follow-up visit and similar questionnaires were also given to two groups of control patients - contemporary patients who had undergone operations not covered by the leaflets, and earlier patients who had undergone operations before the leaflets came into use.

A response rate of 75 per cent was achieved, comprising 100 patients who had received a leaflet and 100 who had not.

There was a significantly higher percentage of overall satisfaction among those who had received leaflets (72 per cent) than those who did not (42 per cent). However, satisfaction was low for both groups for information about complications and late effects, though lowest for the groups who did not receive a leaflet.

The low satisfaction with written information about complications and late effects may have been due to the fact that the leaflets were confined to the effects of the operation rather than those of the underlying diseases.

Certainly this highlights the need for leaflets to be developed which relate closely to the information patients want.

The value of written post-operative information has been emphasised by Savage (1992), who points out that as a result of recent changes in health care delivery, patients often require a higher level of care but are discharged from hospital earlier. This means that patients are expected to perform more self-care, including highly technical procedures. Patient education is one aspect of ensuring continuity of care from hospital to home.

As a prelude to designing a take-home leaflet, Savage investigated patients' views on discharge information provided following oesophageal surgery. Eighteen patients completed questionnaires (a 50 per cent response rate) and she found that 34 per cent of them said there was something they wished they had asked before leaving hospital. These were questions such as 'How much food is "little and often"?' and 'How much weight can I lose until action is taken?'.

These details plus advice ex-patients said they would give to others undergoing the same operation proved to be very useful, leading the researcher to comment:

> *Overall, the survey results and personal comments together gave an accurate insight into individual needs after oesophageal surgery, and this provided the foundation for the content of a discharge advice leaflet.*
> (Savage, 1992, p.27)

A more comprehensive approach, covering both pre- and post-operative information, has been developed by the physiotherapy and occupational therapy departments at the Ceredigion Unit of East Dyfed Health Authority for patients undergoing joint replacement.

The package includes:

1   A letter inviting the patient to attend for a pre-operative appointment.

2   A pre-operative assessment questionnaire to be completed by the patient.

3   A video taking the patient through the stages of joint replacement, including post-operative precautions and available in English and Welsh versions.

4   An *aide-memoire* to be given to the patient detailing post-operative precautions.

The Royal College of Surgeons has recognised the need for good quality information and is designing a series of information booklets for patients about common operations. The first two are on hernia repair and total hip replacement. Their use to patients is being assessed using a combination of detailed questionnaire and interview (Meredith, 1992).

Chronic illness

A useful resource on providing information to people with disabilities is The National Information Forum (see 'Useful addresses'). It aims to:

★   Raise awareness, particularly in the caring professions and voluntary organisations, of the importance of information and of the responsibility for providing it.

★ Encourage research into the most effective means of delivering information.

★ Support training in the skills of providing information.

★ Publicise good practice.

The forum has devised and produced a video-assisted training package for professionals, compiled a guide to sources of information and published two leaflets, one about designing guides to local services and one which looks at the practicalities of providing information for people with disabilities in hospital and following discharge.

For some illnesses, such as asthma, a wealth of information about self-care exists, although much of the research on effectiveness has been carried out in the United States.

For example, Fireman et al (1981) reported a controlled trial of health education in 26 asthmatic children aged 2-14 years. Children and their parents were given four hours of individual instruction in all aspects of asthma management by a trained nurse educator, followed by regular group discussions and telephone access to the educator over the course of one year.

The outcome, as measured by school and medical records, symptom diaries and telephone interviews, was a tenfold reduction in school absence and significantly lower hospital attendances and fewer acute attacks of asthma in the treatment group.

Hilton (1986) describes a number of other similar asthma studies, but concludes:

> *There seems little doubt from the American studies that intensive educational intervention and support can reduce morbidity associated with asthma, but the complexity and cost of these interventions make them unsuitable for large-scale use in primary care.*

> *Research of a more pragmatic nature is required to determine how basic, essential information can be delivered to newly diagnosed asthmatic patients in order to influence their attitudes positively and motivate their behaviour towards optimum self-management.*
>
> *Two logical methods of meeting these goals are the provision of information and support by members of the primary health care team and the development of locally based patients' groups.* (Hilton, 1986, p.47)

The effects on self-management of asthma of a specially prepared book and audio cassette tape were observed in a controlled study of patients with asthma in general practice by Jenkinson et al (1988).

Asthmatic patients selected from eight general practices were invited to take part in a study of problems caused by asthma. Those who agreed were studied for 18 months. All patients kept diary cards to record weekly scores of morbidity and the cards were returned monthly.

After six months a total of 206 patients agreed, and were eligible, to take part in the second part of the study and were allocated to one of four study groups. They were sent a copy of a specially written book, an audio cassette with a similar content, both the book and the tape, or neither.

Questionnaires on the patients' knowledge of the use of bronchodilators and prophylactic drugs (if applicable) and their perceived disability from asthma were administered four times – at the start of the study, six months later (immediately before the educational material was issued), nine months later, and the last a year and a half after the start of the study.

Knowledge about the use of drugs was significantly increased after three months in the groups who received the material and persisted after 12 months. Patients who had been given the tape or the book and tape increased their scores of knowledge of drugs more than did patients given the book alone. Patients given both the book and the tape preferred the book even though they learnt more from the tape.

An educational package for schizophrenic sufferers and their families and friends won a competition sponsored by May and Baker pharmaceuticals and is described by Hilton (1990). The package originated from the assumption that

> ... *information should be made available to sufferers of schizophrenia and that debate and discussion about the problem should not exclude them.* (p.28)

The package includes a number of components:

1   A booklet outlining the nature of schizophrenia, giving an account of possible causes and explaining what can be done to help both sufferers and carers. It includes a list of national organisations interested in schizophrenia and the format for a care plan that can be used by the sufferer or carer. The booklet can be given at any stage of the treatment process and can be used as a tool for discussion.

2   An audio-tape recording with the same content as the booklet. It includes accounts of the personal experiences of sufferers and relatives and has proved useful in staff training.

3   A public display board aimed at exploding some of the myths associated with schizophrenia and encouraging understanding among the general public.

4   A small pamphlet designed for general distribution to heighten public awareness and reduce stigma. It contains basic facts and sources of help. This was distributed via GPs and health, social and voluntary service premises.

5   Literature for a relatives' support group comprising a format for seven consecutive weekly meetings.

This multi-dimensional approach to education ensures that different types of people in various circumstances are able to gain access to information and use it in a way which satisfies their own particular needs.

One important group of people often neglected are the relatives and friends of patients, yet these frequently have care responsibilities and need information to help them carry out their tasks effectively.

A small study designed to find out the type of information required by relatives of elderly patients at a mental health unit is described by Harrison and Smith (1990). The researchers distributed a questionnaire including structured response and open-ended questions to the 15 available relatives or friends of patients in the ward at the time of the study. Eleven of these were returned. Seventeen nurses were also given a similar questionnaire and 15 of these were returned.

Information specifically requested by relatives included the action and side effects of medication, details of the patient's illness, addresses and telephone numbers of day centres, support groups and other voluntary organisations and advice on how to cope with the anxiety and frustration provoked by their relative's illness.

Other relatives wanted to know about the financial assistance that might be available and details of the ward routine and visiting times.

As a result of the project, the researchers developed an information resource file for use by nurses and other staff having direct contact with relatives, friends and visitors. This contained:

★ ward and hospital information

★ details of hospital staff

★ common illnesses among elderly people

★ visual and hearing problems

★ diets and dental care

★ health promotion and exercise

★ useful telephone numbers

★ support for carers

★ financial help available

★ advice on home security.

The file was structured so that items could be copied and given to those visiting patients.

Information about drugs

Patients and relatives consistently express a desire for information about medication, particularly written information. Morris and Groft (1982) reviewed data from 12 studies with a variety of samples and types of medication and showed that an average of approximately 75 per cent of patients wanted written information with their medication.

Unfortunately some health professionals worry that this kind of information may be harmful to patients, particularly information about the potential side effects of medication.

However, studies have shown that telling patients about side effects does not increase their incidence. For example, a review by Morris (1982) showed that only one in eight studies produced evidence of increased side effects.

Others worry that information about possible side effects might frighten patients and put them off taking their prescribed medication, but studies have shown that this is not the case (for example, DiMatteo and DiNicola, 1982).

Giving patients written information about their medication helps to overcome a number of problems. For example:

★ Memory retention can be poor, particularly when a person is under stress.

★ Responsibility for giving information may be unclear. The doctor may think it lies with the pharmacist and vice-versa. One or the other may forget some aspect.

★ The information can be quite complicated and involved, covering, for example, how much to take and when, how long to take it for, precautions, possible side effects, what to do if these occur, what to do if doses are missed or too much is taken, how to recognise if the medicine is not working and what to do about it.

Providing patients with insufficient information about medication seems to be widespread and could have serious consequences. A survey of almost 9,000 patients in 1986 revealed that 55 per cent did not know exactly how, when or with what to take their medication. Eighty per cent of them knew nothing about potential side effects (Busson and Dunn, 1986).

Adverse effects (any noxious change in a patient's condition which necessitates either reducing or stopping therapy and which may itself require treatment) affect up to 18 per cent of patients in hospitals and are thought to account for one consultation in 40 in general practice (George, Gibbs and Waters, 1992).

Researchers at Southampton University have developed information leaflets for several types of commonly prescribed medicines and assessed their impact in a number of studies. Leaflets for penicillins, non-steroidal anti-inflammatory drugs, B-adrenoceptor antagonists, inhaled bronchodilators of the B-agonist type, diuretics and benzodiazepines were produced and given to appropriate patients in five towns near Southampton. In three control towns no leaflets were issued.

These patients were contacted between one and two weeks after consultation and interviewed in their homes. With the exception of the name of the medicine concerned, patients who received leaflets were more knowledgeable than others who did not. The greatest single effect was on the level of satisfaction reported by patients concerning the information they had been given about their medicines.

References for these studies and further details are given in George, Gibbs and Waters, 1992.

Health education

Many health professionals have a responsibility to give out advice and information about how to keep healthy, particularly health promotion officers and, increasingly, primary health care workers.

Although there is a large body of research on the subject, many issues, such as how to help people change their attitudes and behaviour, how to assess the impact of health promotion material, and the advantages of using different media, are common to patient education generally, and so are covered in other sections of the book.

Having said this, there is research specific to the health education field which can contribute to a greater understanding of how lay people receive information and advice given by health professionals.

One area of this concerns the examination of why patients fail to 'comply' with advice – that is, adopt the practices traditionally advocated by health educators, such as abstaining from smoking, changing diet, increasing exercise, etc.

Recent research draws upon the disciplines of anthropology and sociology in order to consider the social and cultural context within which behaviour occurs. From this perspective, behaviour which seems irrational or fatalistic is found to be meaningful, and in this way an insight can be gained into how changes can be made.

Frankel, Davison and Smith (1991) have coined the term 'lay epidemiology' to describe the process by which people interpret health risks. This refers to:

> . . . *the routine observation and discussion of cases of illness and death in personal networks and the public arena, as well as from formal and informal evidence arising from other sources, such as television and magazines.* (p.428)

The researchers make the interesting observation that responses to health messages can sometimes be swift. For example, reports of salmonella infection in egg yolks in 1988 resulted in widespread media attention and a rapid change in dietary practice – egg consumption fell dramatically.

This can be contrasted with the response to longer-standing health warnings concerning the cholesterol content of eggs. In this case egg consumption per head declined only slightly.

The researchers suggest that this difference in response is due to the public perception of different types of risk, which form the opposite ends of a 'risk continuum'.

At one end of the continuum are acute and easily imagined hazards that can readily be avoided. Such agents are seen as 'poisonous', whether in the sense of food poisoning or as in possessing other toxic effects.

Sufferers from diseases caused by poisonous agents can be seen as victims, with legal protection as an appropriate response. Other recent examples include listeriosis from soft cheeses and hyperactivity in children from tartrazine and other food colouring agents.

At the other end of the continuum of public perception of risk are those 'bad/desirable' activities such as smoking, drinking and eating rich foods, which, although perceived as being bad in some respects, are desirable in others. Here the risks are less immediate and less specific. These practices often relate in some way to the core values within a culture.

The items falling into the categories are not completely fixed and are constantly shifting in response to a variety of influences, including advertising.

The researchers have also identified a considerable amount of public scepticism in relation to health education messages. Many of the doubts expressed are similar to those held by epidemiologists. For example, hereditary susceptibility to heart disease is considered by the lay population to be one of the most important risk factors, yet this is rarely discussed in health education material.

Their study of the way in which lay people make sense of advice about health within the wider social cultural context they inhabit leads the researchers to conclude:

> *It may be preferable for health educators to present the public with a balanced representation of current knowledge, and ignorance, of risks to health. The general population's perception of these issues is considerably more sophisticated than is generally appreciated by health educators. Inappropriate messages can only erode the public's trust in the credibility of health education in the longer term.*
> (Frankel, Davison and Smith, 1991, p.430)

The views of the general public will also be influenced by conflicts between different organisational interests, such as the commercial interests of tobacco and sugar industries and the health interests of the NHS.

The advantage of using qualitative methods, such as unstructured interviews, which get beyond the superficial responses of lay people, has also been demonstrated by other researchers.

Questionnaire surveys have shown that a substantial majority of patients expect their general practitioners to be interested in aspects of their lifestyle, such as alcohol consumption and smoking (for example, Wallace and Hanes, 1984).

The fact that the white paper *Promoting Better Health* and the new contract for GPs encourages them to be involved in health promotion should therefore present few problems, as patients have expressed their acceptance of this interest.

However, Stott and Pill (1990) decided to carry out interviews asking questions additional to those included in the Wallace and Hanes postal survey cited above. They were asked: 'In you opinion, should your family doctor be interested in your weight problems, smoking problems, drinking problems, fitness problems?' They were then asked: 'What makes you say that?'. They were also asked: 'Do you think your doctor should advise you about how to live your life – that is, what we should or should not do to keep healthy?'.

The replies of the respondents - 130 women aged between 25 and 40 and classified as Registrar-General's Social Class four or five - to the fixed-response questions about the appropriateness of GP interest in aspects of their behaviour were similar to those found in earlier research. On weight, 94 per cent thought it appropriate; smoking, 88 per cent; drinking, 90 per cent; fitness, 56 per cent.

However, the high positive response rate concealed a wide range of qualifications and reservations that emerged during subsequent questioning. Overall, about 50 per cent of respondents made qualifying comments. These were of four main types:

★ only if behaviour was linked to current illness/could lead to further problems (53 respondents)

★ only if patient takes initiative/asks for help (12 respondents)

★ but do doctors have the time/resources? (10 respondents)

★ but doctors can only advise; in the end it's 'up to me' (34 respondents).

The researchers conclude:

> *The practical implications of this data are that doctors should not make assumptions about their patients' willingness to consider lifestyle issues in an unrelated consultation. . . . Doctors must therefore always precede such advice by clarifying the patient's beliefs and expectations. . . . (p.130)*

The response of lay people to advice and education about changes in lifestyle involving alcohol, smoking, exercise and diet may be complex, but at least on the surface it appears an easier and more straightforward process to educate them about common illnesses, particularly those affecting children.

A number of studies have shown the value of booklets about child health and sickness. For example, Pike (1980) randomly divided the parents of children under the age of 5 in the practice at the time of the study into an experimental group and a control group.

There were 134 families in each group, and one of the parents from each group was asked to complete a questionnaire on three aspects of childcare: (i) the prevention of illness; (ii) the management of minor illness; (iii) the use of the health service.

All patients were then given a copy of a booklet prepared by the practice on these three aspects of child care. Two or three weeks later the experimental group was asked to complete the same questionnaire again.

When the replies before and after reading the booklet in the experimental group were analysed, all showed a significantly improved score except one relating to a question about which illnesses could be prevented by immunisation.

Usherwood (1991) developed a booklet that provided advice for parents on the home management of cough, fever, sore throat, diarrhoea and vomiting in children and included specific recommendations about when to seek medical help.

The effect of distributing this booklet on the frequency of parent-initiated consultations was evaluated in a randomised controlled trial.

The results showed a reduction in consultations for the symptoms that it addressed, but this was statistically non-significant. There was also a statistically significant reduction in day-time home visits for these symptoms, but a significant increase in out-of-hours consultation for fever, diarrhoea and vomiting.

Although the booklet affected parents' behaviour then, not all its effects were beneficial. As the researcher writes:

> . . . if parents are indeed put off contacting the practice for a feverish child until their anxieties get the better of them in the evening, then this is a most unattractive result for child, parents and doctor. (p.61)

Anderson et al (1980) measured mothers' knowledge and monitored new requests for care following the introduction of a booklet describing the management of six common symptoms in children.

In a randomised control trial, they sent a booklet to half of all families in the practice with at least one child under 5. The number of new requests for care, the place of consultation and the symptoms presented were recorded for both groups for one year.

The results showed that the study group 'demanded significantly fewer home visits' compared with the controls. They also requested fewer surgery consultations for five of the six symptoms described.

Interestingly, however, when questionnaires were administered aimed at finding out what the mothers would do if the illness described in the booklet occurred either to her or her eldest pre-school child, there were no significant differences between the experimental group and the control group.

The researchers suggested this might be due to the parents consulting the booklet when they needed to, resulting in a change in behaviour but not in knowledge (76 per cent of the study group said they had referred to the booklet at some time in the previous 15 months).

Although studies such as these have shown that booklets about common childhood illnesses have some effect on their behaviour and are of some use to parents, it may be worth asking just how much more useful they might be if they were compiled with parents themselves. It is difficult to see how general practitioners can compile booklets offering advice on how to treat childhood illnesses without finding out how lay people view these illnesses and their worries and concerns about them. This is not to say that a GP's views are unimportant, only that parents' views are important too.

At present too much information for patients is put together from a professional point of view. It is aimed at encouraging 'compliance' with the existing system rather then empowering people to use services in a way that is better from their point of view.

Patient empowerment

In Chapter 2, the different types of information were placed on a continuum representing various levels of involvement or input from patients. The aim of providing data to inform or educate was seen to be different from that of providing data to empower the patient. The latter is directed at enabling a person to gain greater control over a situation. In the health care setting, this means enabling patients to become equal partners in the care and treatment process instead of being the traditional passive partner, subservient to the wishes of the health professional who 'knows what is best'.

It is clear that in order to change the present situation, patients and health professionals both will need information. Both partners will have to be helped to devise ways of giving patients more control over their health care.

A useful source of knowledge about the effects that different ways of communicating can have on patients is the body of academic research on doctor-patient communication.

The literature is extensive and much of it is quite technical, but it is possible to summarise aspects of it in order to introduce the findings to a wider audience.

The importance of doctor-patient communication is nicely described by Street (1991, p.541):

> *In spite of sophisticated technologies for medical diagnosis and treatment, talk remains the primary means by which the physician and patient exchange health information. The significance of information sharing in medical consultation is readily apparent. For the doctor, information is crucial for formulating diagnosis and prescribing treatment; for the patient, information fosters an understanding of one's health status which in turn may reduce uncertainty, alleviate concerns and improve*

health. Unfortunately, the exchange of information between the patient and physician is often fraught with problems.

The research on doctor-patient communication can be split into three main parts: (1) models or theories of doctor-patient communication; (2) methods or ways of looking at the medical encounter; (3) what the research suggests is good practice in doctor-patient communication. These parts are not separate because the method is often related to the model and the research findings are linked to both.

Models of doctor-patient communication

Models tend to be defined in relation to the traditional biomedical model, described as follows by Butler, Campion and Cox (1992, p.1145):

> *The objective clinician sets out to take a history, to perform examination and investigation, to make a diagnosis and to prescribe treatment. Little attention is paid to the patient's perspective or the patient's problem, both of which are considered to be an impediment to the diagnostic process. The patient has little influence, and the balance of power lies squarely with the doctor.*

The Health Belief Model (Rosenstock, 1974), for example, attempts to place emphasis on patient variables such as health motivation, cues to motivation, and perceptions concerning the probable consequences of leaving an illness untreated. However, the model has been criticised for leaving the balance of power with the doctor and for not taking account of the broader psychosocial issues which surround a consultation (Tuckett et al, 1985).

Stewart and Roter (1989) describe the doctor-patient consultation in terms of a marketplace transaction, seeing the patient as a 'consumer'. In this model the patient's perspective is of most importance because he or she can choose whether or not to 'purchase' medical care.

Tuckett et al (1985) see the patient as an expert in knowledge about their bodily functioning or the care of their children or relatives, and so also propose that the patient's view is of central importance, albeit for a different reason.

The biopsychosocial model (Engel, 1980) is based upon a systems approach and suggests that it is as important for the physician to study the 'higher level' functions of mind and emotion as it is for him or her to study tissues and organs.

McWhinney's (1989) Transformed Medical Model builds upon this biopsychosocial view of the patient and stresses the importance of the meaning of an illness to the patient as well as the need to diagnose the disease. In this model, power is negotiated between doctor and patient.

The reason these models are useful is because they are illustrations of different ways of thinking about the doctor-patient relationship. They can also be used as justifications for treating patients in particular ways. Often a health professional's 'model' of the profession-patient relationship is below the conscious level of awareness and it is worth trying to bring out some of the hidden assumptions in order to examine their appropriateness.

Methods for analysing doctor-patient communication

Much research on doctor-patient communication is about devising methods of analysing the medical encounter. For example, Korsch et al (1968) adapted Bales' (1950) method of Interaction Process Analysis, which was first developed for understanding the functioning and decision-making of small groups.

The researchers coded every statement observed by either party in the doctor-patient consultations into one of 12 mutually exclusive categories (such as positive affect or affectively neutral) so that patterns could be detected.

Byrne and Long (1976) developed another Bales-type interaction system derived from Flanders' (1960) design for use in classrooms. In this system, 10-second intervals in the consultation were coded as belonging to a mutually exclusive phase of problem solving (for example, scanning, formulating, appraising, developing willingness or readiness to solve problem).

A different approach has been developed from linguistic analysis by Stiles et al (1979). Here the researchers code each utterance in a consultation according to its inferred communicative function – for example, whether it was a disclosure, a question, an interpretation or a confirmation. Summaries of these categories can be made so that a doctor's behaviour can be described as attentive, prescriptive or whatever, either overall or at different stages of the consultation.

One of the problems with the linguistic approach is that it ignores non-verbal behaviour. Other researchers have corrected this bias. For example, Larsen and Smith (1981) examined the degree of 'closeness' between two persons in on interaction (assessing body contact, physical distance, posture, eye contact, etc.) as well as the degree of postural 'relaxation' and the degree of 'responsiveness' to each other.

The various methods which have been devised for measuring doctor-patient communication tend to be weak in one particularly important respect: they ignore the relevance of the content of information provided by doctors. For example, the category 'explanation' or 'information giving' may occur many times during a consultation, but if the doctor is being repetitive, this is not the same as if he or she is making things clearer for the patient.

In order to determine the kind of information the doctor is giving it must be possible to distinguish between different kinds of information and not just treat them all as of equal importance. The value to patients of different kinds of information must be known as well.

An American study which attempted to do this was conducted by Svarstad (1974). She hypothesised that patient compliance would be higher among those who had received a large amount of information about the nature of their condition and the rationale for treatment.

She determined how much information patients had received by considering what theoretical issues a doctor would need to help patients to know what was wrong and why treatment was a good idea.

Svarstad found that very few doctors attempted to give rationales for their treatment proposals. She also found that subsequent compliance with instructions (as measured by patients' reports and detailed bottle checks for each drug at interview) was strongly related to how much doctors told them.

From the point of view of the health professional, another weakness in many of the methods used for studying doctor-patient interaction is that they have been developed by academics and are not usually very accessible to those in a health care setting.

An attempt to overcome this weakness has been made by Butler, Campion and Cox (1992), who have developed a way of recording what doctors say in the consultation room which can be related to training.

Good practice in doctor-patient communication

It is to be expected that studies of issues as complex as doctor-patient communication will have weaknesses, but that does not mean that they can therefore be dismissed as useless. A review of such studies shows that important discoveries have been made. In 'Doctor-patient communication: the Toronto consensus statement', Simpson et al (1991) describe the problems which have been uncovered and make suggestions about the most important things that can be done to improve clinical communication by doctors.

They write that physicians should first encourage patients to discuss their main concerns without interruption or premature closure. This enhances satisfaction and the efficacy of the consultation and yet need not take long: a maximum of two and a half minutes or an average of 90 seconds.

Doctors should also strive to elicit patients' perceptions of the illness and associated feelings and expectations.

The appropriate use of open-ended questions, frequent summaries, clarifications and negotiations are factors that improve the quality and quantity of the information gathered. Other important skills include giving clear explanations, checking the patient's understanding, negotiating a treatment plan and checking patients' attention to compliance.

Further guidelines are provided by Carr (1990), who includes:

★ Clarify how much information patients would like about their condition.

★ Offer an explanation of the patient's condition and the rationale for treatment.

★ Present the treatment regimen and the rationale upon which it is based in language that patients can understand and which allows them to remember what has been said. Two ways of aiding memory are (1) to provide a simple set of written instructions and (2) to encourage patients to repeat the rationale and the treatment regimen in their own words.

★ Help the patient to appreciate the costs and benefits of compliance and non-compliance.

It is important to recognise that guidelines on improving communication between doctors and patients can be used to improve communication between health professionals and patients generally.

Training in communication skills

Those wishing to communicate well need to develop a number of skills. It cannot be assumed that health professionals will automatically know how to provide information in a way which helps patients to become more involved in their treatment and care. In fact, quite the reverse is likely to be true, given that the NHS has a history of provider-led care.

A survey of British medical schools published by Wakeford in 1983 showed that in marked contrast to those in North America, no school in the United Kingdom gave more than minimal training in information giving and collecting, and most offered nothing.

In 1980, the General Medical Council issued guidelines which stressed the need for the initiation and co-ordination of such training throughout the undergraduate medical curriculum and in 1986 the first full-time teacher of communications in a medical school in Britain was appointed at Cambridge.

An experiment in teaching and assessing medical students' communications skills, particularly their information-giving skills, was reported by Morris (1992). The study, which took place at Cambridge Medical School in 1986, aimed to improve students' ability to involve patients in decisions and care.

During the study, students were allocated to experimental and control groups, with the experimental group receiving some special training using various methods of feedback on an ad-hoc basis at opportune moments during their clinical training. The methods included observation and feedback, video feedback and simulated patient teaching, using independent lay teachers.

Experimental and control students in the study were video-recorded consulting with simulated patients at the beginning and end of the clinical course. The videotapes were rated by 28 general practitioners, all of whom were experienced in analysing consultations and the majority of whom were examiners for the Royal College of General Practitioners.

They rated the students on 10 items, including question style, structuring, listening, explaining, checking and involving. The results of assessments of 71 students (34 experimental, 37 control) showed that the experimental group received higher mean scores than the control group on all 10 items on the scale and that in seven cases these differences in scores were statistically significant.

Following the research, the UK Network for Communication in Health Care or COMNET (see 'Useful addresses') was formed. A handbook of communication skills tips is in preparation for medical students.

The need for training in the type of communication skills which encourage patient participation appears to be gaining wider recognition within the NHS. For example, nurses operating a primary nursing system at a medical ward at South Cleveland Hospital developed their skills by giving patients their nursing notes and explaining the treatment and care plan to them. They found:

> *It improves listening and communication skills because all stages of the nursing process are completed with the co-operation of the patient at the bedside.*
> (Ahmed and Alarcon, 1992)

A study aimed at training hospital medical and nursing staff in communication skills and testing the taping of a new pre-discharge interview which was then given to patients took place at Grantham and Kesteven General Hospital in 1992. A report of the findings is available from the College of Health (see 'Useful addresses').

The concept of patient empowerment recognises that patients should be equal partners in the care relationship. So far this section has looked at ways in which health care professionals can improve their communication skills, particularly the way they provide information, so that patients can have more control over their treatment and care.

Patients can also be empowered by receiving communication skills training themselves. They can take part in simulated encounters between patient and health care professional and receive help in dealing with the encounter in a way which makes them feel more in control.

Joint training for patients or other lay people and health professionals could also be an effective way of improving the communication skills of both. This is especially important where lay people are expected to take part in formulating health policy and planning health services.

An example of training of this kind is the two-day training programme for lay and professional service committee members piloted among FHSAs by the Industrial Society in 1993 and called 'Effective handling of complaints'.

Research on the training needs of lay people involved in health has been carried out by the Patients' Association, which has produced a useful booklet, *Training for lay participation in health* (Brotchie and Wann, 1993).

Other ways of empowering patients

There are a number of other ways in which patients can be empowered and it is worth briefly describing some of them.

The King's Fund Centre in 1993 is piloting and evaluating an interactive video system designed to give patients information about the risks and benefits of choices open to them. This system makes information accessible to patients at the time they need to make decisions about treatment with their doctor.

The interactive video is designed to supplement the consultant or general practitioner's explanation about the condition in a way that means that the decision about treatment can be shared between doctor and patient. Interactive video programmes are available for benign prostatic cancer, hyperplasia, choices of surgery for early breast cancer, chemotherapy after surgery for early breast cancer, mild raised blood pressure and the treatment of low back pain (Darkins, 1993).

Patient advocates can help those who find it difficult to speak up for themselves to have a voice. Patient advocacy developed first in the United States and Holland during the 1970s, mainly in the mental health field. In Holland, where psychiatric services are provided in private hospitals, it has involved the development of ward-based patients' councils.

These have been supported by managers who want to communicate with patients in order to improve service quality and also by the government, where members see the movement as an aid in the process of standardising psychiatric hospitals. Legislation has been drawn up which states that each psychiatric hospital in Holland must have a patients' council.

In the United States the movement has developed in opposition to the government rather than with institutional support, as in Holland. It grew out of the separatist organisations of the 1960s, particularly the anti-psychiatry movement. The United States now has many after-care and support services which are run by users and ex-users but receive public funding.

Advocacy can be divided into a number of different types:

★ Citizen advocacy, where skilled volunteers supported by an independent agency work with individuals on a long-term basis.

★ Paid advocacy, where skilled workers are paid by an independent agency to represent the interest of individuals, usually in the short term.

★ Self-advocacy, where, singularly or collectively, individuals work on their own behalf to realise their own interests.

The key element in all of the descriptions is that the advocate is accountable to an independent agency or, in the case of self-advocacy, is clearly working to realise her or his own interest.

Patient advocacy in Britain is developing slowly and there are a growing number of examples of all three types.

For example, there are citizen advocacy schemes involving people with learning difficulties, mental health service patients and elderly people (Butler and Forrest, 1990; Butler, Carr and Sullivan, 1988).

There are a number of examples of paid advocacy schemes in services for Black women (for example, Cornwell and Gordon, 1984).

With the establishment of People First in the mid-1980s, a number of self-advocacy groups have developed for people with learning difficulties (People First, Oxford House, Derbyshire Street, London, E2 6HG, tel 071-739 3890).

Self-advocacy groups have also developed among users of mental health services and these are often termed 'patients' councils' following the Dutch model (Campbell, 1990; Gell, 1990).

There are to date fewer examples of advocates working on behalf of patients in general, but Leeds City Council employs one, along with ten volunteers, to support patients in hospitals and clinics throughout Leeds and the surrounding area (Holmes, 1991).

A growing number of hospitals are employing patient representatives or patient liaison officers to help improve communication between patients and health care staff. Patient representatives can help give a human face to hospital bureaucracy: patients know that someone not directly involved in their care can deal with their concerns and examine the hospital from the patient's viewpoint (McIver, 1993).

Another way of helping patients to voice their opinions and concerns is to set up a patients' forum. Many people who would not feel able to express their views in patient satisfaction surveys can be encouraged to do so using their approach. Clarke (1993) provides a good example in a rehabilitation unit for elderly people.

Finally, there is a growing acceptance by health care professionals of the importance of self-help groups in supporting and empowering patients and relatives, particularly those with chronic or life-threatening illnesses, such as cancer (for example, Speigal, Bloom, Yalom, 1981).

However, research carried out by Bradburn et al (1992) on community-based cancer support groups found that hospital staff 'were inclined to be cautious' in giving information about local support groups to patients rather than making the information freely available to all.

The study found that the 18 local support groups were a considerable resource for cancer patients in the catchment area, offering mutual support together with a wide range of other services which were not provided elsewhere.

One of the recommendations made by the researchers was that routes of communication should be established between hospital staff and support groups in order to promote mutual education and understanding.

A report describing how partnerships between health promotion workers and self-help groups can be developed has been produced by the National Self Help Support Centre (1991).

Summary

In sum, there exists a massive amount of literature about information provision in the health field. This addresses different questions and issues, but common themes occur and it is possible to abstract useful guidance from the different areas.

For example, the field of public relations is knowledgeable about the wider issue of information flow and communications and about layout, design and clarity of writing style.

In patient education, an understanding has developed of how individuals retain information, learn new practices and change their behaviour. This has also happened to some extent in health education, although the emphasis has been on the way that people in general interpret information according to the communities they live in and the lifestyles they follow. As well, a good understanding of the use of different media has been gained in these areas.

In research on doctor-patient communication, the issue of what makes a good consultation has been studied in some detail - too much detail to make it accessible to most health care professionals. However, it is possible to extract guidelines on what patients find helpful and on what they consider to be good and bad communication in order to help effect improvements in this area.

By studying the different areas of patient information, then, it is possible to find out about the range that health care professionals may need to provide to patients and also to build upon the expertise developed in the various areas.

5 GETTING FEEDBACK ABOUT PATIENT INFORMATION

Surveys of patients about their views of services rarely cover the subject of information provision in enough detail. The usual practice is to include a question or two asking whether patients felt the information was 'satisfactory' or whether they felt they had received enough information.

This either is unanswerable (what does 'satisfactory' mean?) or deals with only one issue – that of amount of information – and it is debatable whether this is the most important. There is a wide range of issues to choose from, for example:

★   is the information given at the right time?

★   is it given at the right place?

★   is it understandable?

★   is it comprehensive?

★   is it accurate?

★   is it up-to-date?

★   is it ethical (e.g., does it comply with equal opportunities guidelines, is it scaremongering or victim-blaming)?

★   is it relevant from the patient's point of view?

★   is the most appropriate medium used?

★ is there provision for those who do not read English?

★ is the opportunity to get further information or support provided?

A number of questions can be devised, bearing in mind these issues; some further examples are provided at the end of this chapter.

Although the process of devising the most appropriate questions to ask patients is one of the most important aspects of asking patients for their views on information provision, it is not the only one.

Aim of information

Another important aspect is to be clear about the intended aim of the information provided: is it to inform, to educate, or to help patients gain more control over the treatment and care process? Information may have more than one aim, but it will be difficult to evaluate the effectiveness of the information provided if the aim is unclear (see Chapter 2).

This will also be true if patients are expected to judge whether the information is 'satisfactory' because what this really means is whether it fulfils its function. How are patients to answer the question if they are not aware of why information is being provided? Is it to inform patients of what health services are available? Then does it do this or does it in some way fail in this aim from their point of view?

Target group

Research carried out in the health education field has shown that for information to be effective it should be carefully designed to suit people's particular needs.

What comprises the significant groups or categories of people will vary from circumstance to circumstance, but factors such as age, gender, social class, economic status, religion and lifestyle will be important variables, as well as whether the information is aimed at other professionals, voluntary groups, carers or patients. Among patients, the particular stage their illness has reached may produce different information needs.

These factors should also be taken into consideration when users' views are sought. In other words, clarity about what are the crucial categories or groups using the information is necessary.

When these have been identified it will be possible to decide which method to use to obtain feedback because not all methods work equally well with everyone.

Method

The use of different methods to obtain feedback from health service users has been covered in detail elsewhere (see especially McIver, 1991) and so only a brief outline will be given here.

The key point to remember is that there are two main types of method – quantitative and qualitative – and these are suited to different purposes.

Quantitative methods are useful for collecting data to answer questions asking 'How many?', such as 'How many people received this leaflet?' or 'How many people found it difficult to understand this leaflet?'.

These methods collect information in numerical form, such as the analysis of documents giving throughput figures, questionnaires with boxes for the respondent to tick or interview schedules where the respondent has to reply by choosing from a list of alternatives (structured questionnaires and interviews).

Qualitative methods are useful for collecting data to answer 'Why?' questions, such as 'Why are people not receiving this leaflet?' or 'Why do people not understand this leaflet?'.

These methods collect information in narrative form, such as interviews which allow respondents to describe in their own words what they think and discussion groups where those present explore their views on an issue.

Often research questions demand answers of both a statistical and explanatory nature and a combination of methods is called for, such as discussion groups followed by structured interviews or a questionnaire with both limited-response and open questions.

Within these two main categories of method, choice will depend upon a number of considerations, such as the budget and expertise available, but a major factor will be the target group.

For example, there would be no point in posting or handing out self-completion questionnaires to those who would probably be unable to complete them (for instance, those with a low level of literacy and those who find forms confusing, such as many elderly people and those who are taking drugs which affect their concentration). Interviews would have to be used in cases like these.

Project plan

The process of getting feedback from users needs to be well planned in order to be successful. Five main stages are involved in each project. These are:

★ setting up the project

★ collecting the data

★ coding and analysing the data

★ writing the report

★ disseminating the results.

These stages should be timetabled and costed so that time and money do not run out before the end of a project, something that can happen quite easily to the inexperienced. Planning a user feedback project has been covered in detail in McIver (1991).

Acting upon the results

When planning a project to get user feedback about the quality of information provision, a commitment should be made by senior management to act upon the results of the research, otherwise it will have been a waste of time and money. In practice this means thinking through in advance what the possible outcomes of the research might be and planning for each eventuality.

Devising questions

Before giving some examples of questions to ask users about quality of information, a few qualifying remarks are in order.

Firstly, the questions provided are examples of general ones to ask about the quality of information provision and are not devised for a particular situation, such as evaluating the effectiveness of a particular type of information.

Secondly, questions would normally be drawn up after a review of the results of qualitative research (such as unstructured interviews and discussion groups) on what patients think about information provided by health services. Unfortunately very little research of this kind has been carried out. Most has covered information provision in a superficial manner, uncovering only the fact that patients are dissatisfied.

By drawing upon research in other health fields, such as public relations, health promotion, patient education and doctor-patient communication, however, it has been possible to reveal what is likely to improve information provision from the patients' point of view. It has also been possible to glean some ideas for example questions.

Those intending to work seriously on this subject should consider using qualitative methods to find out what patients and other service users consider to be good quality information.

Thirdly, those wishing to use the example questions will need to test them out with users (pilot them), particularly if a self-completion questionnaire is being devised. Advice on the design and testing of questionnaires, sampling procedures, etc. should be sought (see McIver, 1991; Dixon and Carr-Hill, 1989, Fitzpatrick, 1991, for further information).

Example questions to ask service users about quality of information

1   Did you receive the information about. . . (the subject)?

2   When did you receive the information?

3   Was this the best time to receive it, or would you have preferred it at another time?
(a) This was the best time to receive it
(b) I would have preferred to receive it at another time
If (b), when would you have preferred to receive it?

4   Were you happy about the circumstances in which you received the information?
Yes
No
If no, please explain what made you unhappy.

5 Did it explain things in a way you could understand?

6 Did it cover all the issues that you hoped it would?

7 Did it cover all the things that you wanted to know about?

8 Did it raise any worries in your mind?
Yes
No
If yes, please describe these worries.

9 Did the information upset you in any way?
Yes
No
If yes, in what way did it upset you?

10 Would you prefer/would it be easier for you to receive the information in a different way (e.g., by cassette tape or video)?

11 Do you still have questions you want to ask about (the subject)?

12 Do you know who to contact to get answers to any further questions you may have?

13 Do you have any suggestions about ways we could improve the information we provide about (the subject)?

6 CONCLUSION

Patient information is beginning to receive the attention it deserves, but at present its provision is patchy, unco-ordinated and of varying quality. There are some examples of good practice, but too much poor quality material and 'reinvention of wheel' exists.

Part of the problem is that research and development in this area has been carried out across a number of disciplines. Without an overview of what has been developed and the extent of existing knowledge about what patients want, it is difficult for health care professionals to identify weak areas. This book has attempted to rectify this situation by drawing together examples of good practice from a number of areas.

As well as the issue of the different *types* of information which health professionals should be providing, there is the issue of *how* this information should be provided; that is, the way information flows to patients.

Who is responsible for giving information to whom? Are there ways of checking whether information is flowing correctly, apart from asking patients or expecting them to say something when the system fails? Is the information provided by different professionals or departments consistent?

Another part of the problem is that information has rarely been developed *with* patients. This is probably because, until recently, mechanisms for getting patient feedback have been underdeveloped in the NHS due to the dominant view of patients as passive receivers of health care.

What it means is that information may not be appropriate or relevant to patients and so they may not find it as useful as health care professionals believe.

This view of patients as passive receptors of professionals' instructions about treatment and care needs to be replaced by one which has been shown by social researchers to be closer to reality.

This is a view of patients or 'lay people' as active managers of their own health care, consulting a wide range of people for medical advice and for suggestions on the use of medications – a view which accepts that patients know a lot about the way they feel and that they bring anxieties and expectations which they would like health care providers to address.

It also means accepting a view of health care in which the mind is as important as the body. Anxiety and emotional distress can be caused by physical symptoms and can in turn be the cause of symptoms.

By developing information with patients it will be possible to address their anxieties and concerns and so improve the quality of the information provided.

The development of ways to monitor quality will ensure continuing improvement. Obtaining feedback from patients is an important way of doing this.

Developments in 'patient satisfaction' research suggest that a number of detailed questions about an issue are more useful to those wishing to improve service quality than general questions about satisfaction. Examples of the kinds of questions to ask patients have been given in the booklet.

In sum, those wishing to improve information provision to patients may find the following steps useful:

1 Think about patient information within the wider context of communication (see Chapter 4).

2 Review what information is already being provided to patients by the organisation and also what relevant information is being provided by other organisations.

3 Consider the different areas of information provision (see Chapter 4).

4 Prioritise (e.g., decide whether to improve areas of existing information provision or extend provision to other areas).

5 Build a programme of information improvement based upon the priorities.

6 Within individual areas, decide on the aim (whether patient information, patient education, empowerment, etc.) and identify target groups/populations (Chapter 2).

7 Think about what might be the most appropriate medium or combination (see Chapter 3).

8 Develop information with patients/members of target group.

9 Monitor users' views on the quality of the information provided on a regular basis to catch any changes in the situation (see Chapter 5).

10 Evaluate the effectiveness of the information in fulfilling the original aim and in the level of detail required (see Chapter 2).

USEFUL ADDRESSES

The Acorn Project

Solent School of Health Studies
St Mary's Hospital
Newport
Isle of Wight
Tel: 0983 524081, ext 4479

Consumer Health Information Consortium

Highcroft Cottage
Romsey Road
Winchester
Hampshire
SO22 5DH
Tel: 0962 849100

College of Health

St Margaret's House
21 Oldford Road
London
E2 9PL
Tel: 081-983 1225

Health Education Authority

Hamilton House
Mabledon Place
London
WC1H 9TX
Tel: 071-383 3833

The Help For Health Trust

Highcroft Cottage
Romsey Road
Winchester
Hampshire
SO22 5DH
Tel: 0962 849100

The National Information Forum

Charitybase
50 Westminster Bridge Road
London
SE1 7QY
Tel: 071-721 7672

UK Network for Communication in Health Care (COMNET)

Katherine Weare
Director of the Health Education
Unit
School of Education
The University of Southampton
S09 5NH
Tel: 0703 593768

REFERENCES

Adams L et al. Community participation in health promotion, Health Education Authority, 1990.

Alderman C. Help For Health. *Nursing Standard*, Aug 14, vol.5 no.47, 1991, p.22-23.

Ahmed D, Alarcon A. Whose plan is it anyway? *Nursing Times*, 1 Jan, 1992, vol. 88, no.1, p.60.

Anderson J, Morrell D, Avery A, Watkins C. Evaluation of a patient education manual. *British Medical Journal.* Vol.281, 4 Oct 1980, p.924-926.

Bailey, William et al. A randomized trial to improve self-management practices of adults with asthma. Archives Intern Medicine. Vol.150, August 1990, p.1664-1668.

Bales R. Interaction Process Analysis. Addison-Wesley Press, Cambridge, 1950.

Barnes E. *People in Hospital*. London: MacMillan, 1961 (1981).

Bernadt M, Gunning L, Quenstedt M. Patients' access to their own psychiatric records. *British Medical Journal.* Vol.303, 19 Oct 1991, p.967.

Bhopal R S et al. Evaluation of a practice information leaflet. *Family Practice*, vol.7, no.2, 1990, p.132-137.

British Market Research Bureau. 'Patient satisfaction amongst hospital in-patients: A report on qualitative research.' January 1991. 'Report on a survey of hospital in-patients in three District Health Authorities.' Nov 1991. Copies of these reports can be obtained from Eastbourne HA, 9 Upperton Road, Eastbourne, BN21 2BH. Also in the King's Fund Centre library.

Boore J. Pre-operative care of patients. *Nursing Times.* 24 March 1977, p.409-411.

Bradburn J. et al. Community based cancer support groups: an undervalued resource? *Clinical Oncology*, no.4, 1992, p.377-380.
Brotchie J, Wann M. Training for lay participation in health. The Patients Association, 1993. 18 Victoria Park Square, Bethnal Green, London, E2 9PF. Tel: 081-981 5676/5695.

Budd J, McCron R. The role of the mass media in health education. Centre for Mass Communication Research, for the Health Education Council, 1982.

Bunker T. An information leaflet for surgical patients. Annals of the Royal College of Surgeons, 1983. Vol.65, p.242-3.

Busson M, Dunn A P. Patient knowledge about prescribed medicines. *Pharmaceutical Journal*. Vol.236, 1986, p.624-6.

Butler N, Campion P, Cox A. Exploration of doctor and patient agendas in general practice consultations. *Social Science & Medicine*, 1992, vol 35, no.9, p.1145-1155.

Butler K, Carr S, Sullivan F. Citizen Advocacy: a powerful partnership. A handbook on setting up and running citizen advocacy schemes. National Citizen Advocacy, 1988.

Butler K, Forrest M. Citizen Advocacy for people with disabilities. In Winn L. (ed) Power to the people. London: King's Fund Centre, 1990.

Byrne P, Long B. Doctors Talking to Patients. HMSO, London, 1976.

Campbell P. Mental health self-advocacy. In Winn L (ed). Power to the people. London: King's Fund Centre, 1990.

Carr A. Compliance with medical advice. *British Journal of General Practice*. September 1990, p.358-360.

Cartwright A. *Human Relations and Hospital Care*. London: Routledge Kegan Paul, 1964.

Clarke M. Speaking up. *Nursing Times*. 13 Jan, vol 89, no.2, 1993, p.42-44.

Close A. Patient Education: a literature review. Journal of Advanced Nursing. Vol.13, 203-213, 1988.

Close A. Learning Package: patient education and information giving, 1993. WMRHA, Arthur Thomson House, 146, Hagley Road, Birmingham, B16 9PA. Tel: 021 456 1444, ext 1058.

Cohen S A. Patient Education - a review of the literature. *Journal of Advanced Nursing*, 6, 1-18, 1981.

Cornwell J. Gordon P. An experiment in advocacy: the Hackney multi-ethnic women's health project. London: King's Fund Centre, 1984.

Cutts, M. Patient Information Project: Final Report. 1991. Northern and Mental Health Health Unit, St George's Hospital, Morpeth, NE61 2NU, Tel: 0670 512121. Copy in King's Fund Centre library.

Darkins A. Helping patients share decisions with their doctors. *King's Fund News*. March, 1993.

Deardorff W. Computerised health education: a comparison with traditional formats. *Health Education Quarterly* 13(1), 1986, 61-72.

Diamatteo M R, Dinicola D D. Achieving Patient Compliance: the psychology of the medical practitioner's role. New York: Pergamon, 1982.

Dixon P, Carr-Hill R. Customer feedback surveys: an introduction to survey methods. Part 2 of The NHS and its customers. University of York: Centre for Health Economics, 1989.

Edwards M. Satisfying patients' needs for surgical information. *British Journal of Surgery*. Vol.77, April 1990, p.463-465.

Engel G. The clinical application of the biopsychosocial model. *American Journal of Psychiatry* 1980, 137, p.535-544.

Fireman et al. Teaching self-management skills to asthmatic children and their parents in an ambulatory care setting. *Pediatrics*, 1981, vol.68, p.341-8.

Fitzpatrick R. Surveys of patient satisfaction: II-Designing a questionnaire and conducting a survey. *British Medical Journal*, vol.302, 11 May 1991, 1129-1132.

Flanders N. Interaction Analysis in the Classroom: a manual for observers. University of Michigan Press. Ann Arbor, MI, 1960.

Frankel S, Davison C, Smith G D. Lay epidemiology and the rationality of responses to health education. *British Journal of General Practice*, 1991, 41, p.428-430.

Gagliano M. A literature review on the efficacy of video in patient education. *Journal of Medical Education*, vol.63, October 1988, p.785-792.

Gann R, Needham C. Promoting choice: Consumer health information in the 1990s. Winchester: CHIC, 1991.

Gann R. Consumer health information: Growth of an information specialism. Journalism of Documentation, 47(3), 284-308, 1991.

Gatchel R. Impact of a videotaped dental fear-reduction program on people who avoid dental treatment. *J Am. Dent Ass.* 112, 1986, p.218-221.

OBTAINING THE VIEWS OF USERS OF HEALTH SERVICES ABOUT QUALITY OF INFORMATION

Shirley McIver

King's Fund Centre

Published by the King's Fund Centre
126 Albert Street, London NW1 7NF
Telephone: 071-267 6111

ISBN 1 85717 051 2

A CIP catalogue record for this book is available from the British Library

Distributed by Bournemouth English Book Centre (BEBC)
PO Box 1496
Poole
Dorset
BH12 3YD

The King's Fund Centre is a service development agency which promotes
improvements in health and social care. W do this by working with people in
health and social services, in voluntary agencies, and with the users of these
services. We encourage people to try out new ideas, provide financial or
practical support to new developments, and enable experiences to be shared
through workshops, conferences, information services and publications. Our
aim is to ensure that good developments in health and social care are widely
taken up. The King's Fund Centre is part of the King's Fund.

Gell C. User group involvement. In Winn (ed). Power to the people. London: King's Fund Centre, 1990.

Gill M, Scott D. Can patients benefit from reading copies of their doctors' letters about them? *British Medical Journal*. 1986, 293, p.1278-9.

Gilley, M. An eye for the facts. *The Health Service Journal*. 1 Nov, 1990, p.1654-5.

Glasser B. (Almost) Everything You Wanted to Know About Producing Your Own Patient Information Material. 1992. Available from: Patient Information Programme, Royal Free Hospital, Hampstead.

George C, Gibbs S, Waters W. The effects of prescription information leaflets for commonly used medicines. In *Health Promotion: the role of the professional in the community. Proceedings of a symposium*, 1992. Health Promotion Research Trust. 49-53, Regent Street, Cambridge, CB2 1AB. Tel: 0223 69636. See also reference. Morris P.

Harrison N, Smith B. Information Wanted. *Nursing Times*, 7 Feb 1990, vol.86, no.6, p.46-48.

Hicks A. Pick It Up With The Shopping. *The Health Service Journal*. 14 March, 1991, p.24.

Hilton S. A health education package for schizophrenia sufferers and their families and friends. *Community Psychiatric Journal*, vol.10, no.4, Aug 1990, p.22-29.

Hilton S. Patient education in asthma. *Family Practice*. Vol.3, no.1, 1986, p.44-48.

Hogbin B, Fallowfield L. Getting it taped: the 'badnews' consultation with cancer patients. *British Journal of Hospital Medicine*, 1989, 41, p.330-333.

Holmes P. The patient's friend. *Nursing Times*. 8 May, vol 87, no.19, 1991, p.16-17.

Horder J, Moore G. The Consultation and Health Outcomes. *British Journal of General Practice*, Nov 1990, p.442-3.

Hull D. A Patient's Guide to NHS Changes. *NHS Management Bulletin*. No.29, Jan 1990, p.5.

Jenkinson D et al. Comparison of effects of a self management booklet and audio cassette for patients with asthma. *British Medical Journal*, vol.297, 23 July 1988, p.267-268.

Jones L, Leneman L, MacLean U. *Consumer Feedback for the NHS: A Literature Review*. London: King Edward's Hospital Fund for London, 1987.

Kempson E. Review Article: Consumer Health Information Services. *Health Libraries Review*. Vol.1, 1984, p.127-144.

Korsch B et al. Gaps in doctor-patient communications: doctor-patient interaction and patient satisfaction. Pediatrics, 42, 855, 1968.

Larsen K. Smith C. Assessment of non-verbal communication in the patient-physician interview. *Journal of Family Practice*, 12, 1981, p.481-488.

Lindeman C. Nursing intervention with the pre-surgical patient. Nursing Research, 21, 1972, 196-209.

Luker K, Caress A. Rethinking patient education. *Journal of Advanced Nursing*, vol.14, 1989, 711-718.

Marsh G N. The Practice Brochure: a patient's guide to team care. BMJ. Vol.281, 13 Sept 1980, p.730-732.

Mayberry J F, Rose J, Rhodes J. Assessment of a patient information booklet an ulcerative colitis. *Italian Journal of Gastroenterology*, vol.21, 1989, p.193-195.

Melamed B et al. Reduction of fear-related dental management problems with use of filmed modeling. *J. Am. Dent Ass.* 90, 1975, p.822-826.

Melamed B et al. Effects of film modeling on the reduction of anxiety-related behaviour in individuals varying in level of previous experience in the stress situation. *J Consult. Clin. Psych.* 46, 1978, p.1357-1367.

Meredith P. Patient Information Project, Work in Progress, 1992. Surgical Audit Unit, Royal College of Surgeons.

McGhee A. *The Patient's Attitude to Nursing Care*. Edinburgh and London: Livingstone, 1961.

McIntyre K, Miller J, Sullivan F. The 1990 Contract: Have Patients Noticed? *Health Bulletin*. 50,1, Jan 1992, p.7-13.

McIver S. Counting Customers or Making Customers Count? *Critical Public Health*. Vol.3, no.1, 1992, p.16-21.

McIver S. Obtaining the views of users of health services. London: King's Fund Centre, 1991.

McIver S. The patient representative project interim report. Jan, 1993. NAHAT, Head Office, Birmingham Research Park, Vincent Drive, Birmingham, B15 2SQ.

McWhinney I. The need for a transformed clinical method. In Stewart M. and Roter D (eds). Communicating with medical patients. Sage, London, 1989.

Morris L A, Groft S. Patient package inserts: a research perspective. In Melmon K (ed) *Drug therapeutics: concepts for clinicians*. N. York: Elseimer, 1982.

Morris L A. A review and perspective on patient package inserts. In Morgan J. (ed) *Proper prescribing: conflicting signals*. Levington, Mass: Lexington Books, 1982.

Morris P. The development and evaluation of training in health education and information-giving skills for medical students and doctors. In The Health Promotion Research Trust, *Health Promotion: the role of the professional in the community*. 1992. 49-53, Regent Street, Cambridge, CB2 1AB.

NCHR. A guide to community health projects. National Community Health Resource, 1987, 57, Charlton Street, London, NW1 IHU. 071-383 3841.

National Self Help Support Centre. Self help groups. A way to health. 1991. Reviewed in *Community Health Action*, issue 19, Spring 1991, p.19-20.

Neville R, Mason C. The Evaluation of a General Practice Patient Information Leaflet - A Pilot Study. *Health Bulletin*. Vol.45, p.185-189, 4 July 1987.

N E Thames RHA. Health in any language - a guide to producing health information for non-English speaking people. 1990, Inhouse Public Relations, 40 Eastbourne Terrace, London.

North Manchester HA. Guidelines for the production of written information. June 1991. Available from: North Manchester Health Promotion, Beech Mount, Harpurney, Manchester, M9 1XS, Tel: 061-203 4101.

Parrot J, Strathdee G, Brown P. Patient access to psychiatric records: the patient's view. *Journal of the Royal Society of Medicine*, 1988, vol.81, 520-2.

Pike L. Teaching parents about child health using a practice booklet. *Journal of the Royal College of General Practitioners*, 1980, 30, (Sept), p.517-519.

Rayner C. Reality and Expectation of the British National Health Service Consumer. *Journal of Advanced Nursing*. Vol.4, 1979, p.69-77.

RIPACS. An evaluation of patient information literature in Brighton Health Authority. Royal Institute of Public Administration Consultancy Services, 1987. Copy in King's Fund Centre library.

Robinson S, Roberts M. A Women's Health Shop: A Unique Experiment. *British Medical Journal*. Vol.291, 27 July, 1985, p.255-256.

Rosenstock I. Historical origins of the Health Belief Model: orgins and correlates in psychological theory. *Health Education Monographs 2*, 1974, p.336-353.

Rutherford, W. Gabriel R. Audit of outpatient letters. *British Medical Journal.* Vol.303, 19 Oct 1991, p.968.

Rylance G. Patients' right to know. *British Medical Journal.* Vol.303, 19 Oct 1991, p.608-9.

Sandler D et al. Is an information booklet for patients leaving hospital helpful and useful? *British Medical Journal.* Vol.298, 1 April 1989, p.870-874.

Savage J. Advice to take home. *Nursing Times.* Vol.88, no.38, 16 Sept 1992, p.24-27.

Shenkin B N, Warner D C. Giving the patient his medical record: a proposal to improve the system. *New England Journal of Medicine*, 1973, 289, p.688-690.

Silver R. *Guidelines: Better Information Literature For Hospital Patients.* King's Fund Centre, 1991.

Simpson M. et al. Doctor-patient communication: the Toronto Consensus Statement. *British Medical Journal*, vol 303, 30 Nov, 1991, p.1385-7.

Speigel D, Bloom Y, Yalom I. Group support for patients with metastatic cancer: a randomised prospective outcome study. *Arch. Gen. Psychiatry*, 1981, 38, p.527-33.

Stoller R. Patients' responses to their own case reports. *J American Psychoanalytical Ass.* 1988, vol.36, p.371-91.

Sweetland J. In the Know. *Nursing Times.* Vol.86, no.33, Aug 15 1990, p.36-38.

Stanley I, Tongue B. Providing information and detecting concerns about health in general practice populations using a computer system in the waiting area. *British Journal of General Practice*, Vol. 41, 1991, p.499-503.

Stevens Garding B et al. Effectiveness of a program of information and support for myocardial infarction patients recovering from home. *Heart and Lung*, vol.17, no.4, July 1988, p.335-362.

Stott N, Pill R. 'Advise Yes, Dictate No.' Patients' views on health promotion in the consultation. *Family Practice*, vol.7, no.2, 1990, p.125-131.

Street, R. L. Information-giving in medical consultations: the influence of patients' communicative styles and personal characteristics. *Social Science & Medicine*, 1991, vol 32, no.5, p.541-548.

Stewart M, Roter D (eds). *Communicating with medical patients.* Sage, London, 1989.

Stiles W et al. Interaction exchange structure and patient satisfaction with medical interviews. *Medical Care*, 17, 1979, p.667-679.

Svarstad B. The doctor-patient encounter: an observational study of communication and outcome. Doctoral Dissertation, Department of Sociology, University of Wisconsin, Madison, WI. 1974. Described in Tuckett D & Williams A. Approaches to the measurement of explanation and information-giving in medical consultations: A review of empirical studies. *Soc. Sci Med.* vol.18, no.7, 1984, p.571-580.

SW Thames RHA, Mid-Downs HA. Mapping the Way to Better Communications. June 1992. Available from: Communications Directorate, SW Thames RHA, 40 Eastbourne Terrace, London, W2 3QR.

Tuckett D et al. *Meetings between experts: an approach to sharing ideas in medical consultations.* Tavistock, London. 1965.

Usherwood T. Development and randomized controlled trial of a booklet of advice for parents. *British Journal of General Practice*, 1991, 41, (Feb), p.58-62.

Uzark K et al. Use of videotape to promote parenting of infants with serious congenital heart defects. Patient Education Council, 7, 1985, 11-119.

Wakeford R E. Communications skills training. In Pendleton D, Hasler J. (eds). *Doctor-patient communication.* Academic Press, London, 1983.

Wallace P, Haines A. General practitioners and health promotion: what patients think. *British Medical Journal*, 1984, 289, p.534-536.

Weinberger M et al. Can the provision of information to patients with osteoarthritis improve functional status? *Arthritis & Rheumatism*, vol.32, no.12 (December) 1989, p.1577-1583.

Winkler F. Consumerism and Information in Winn (ed). *Power to the People.* King's Fund Centre, 1990.

Zweifler A J, Kaunisto C A. Education of the hypertensive patient: the Ann Arbor approach. *Journal of Hypertension.* Vol.7, (supp.3) 1989, p.89-91.

Printed by The College Hill Press Limited (TU), London and Worthing